Stop Smoking:
It's a Doddle

ABOUT THE AUTHOR

Daniel L McDermid is a graduate in psychology. After his degree he studied with the London College of Clinical Hypnotherapy to become a practitioner of Cognitive Behavioural Hypnotherapy. He runs Leeds Hypnotherapy Clinic in Leeds city centre in West Yorkshire, England and is a member of the British Society of Clinical Hypnosis (BSCH).

(www.leeds-hypnotherapy-clinic.co.uk)

For my wife Kirstine and son Seth

Published by York Place Media
Lion House, 41, York Place,
Leeds LS1 2ED, West Yorkshire, England

First published 2015

Book design: York Place Media
www.yorkplacemedia.co.uk

Cover photograph by Richard Wilson, Leeds

Printed in England by Jellyfish Solutions Ltd.
Swanmore, Hants.

ISBN: 978-1-909826-05-2

Stop Smoking: It's a Doddle

**A Cognitive Behavioural Approach
supported by Clinical Hypnotherapy**

By Daniel L McDermid

CONTENTS

Section One

Section Two

Section Three

AUTHOR'S NOTES

● This book expands on issues outlined on my website leeds-hypnotherapy-clinic.co.uk *and reflects the advice that I offer to clients who visit me seeking help to stop smoking.*

The treatment I provide at the clinic derives from principles of cognitive behavioural hypnotherapy (CBH) and uses rational emotive behavioural therapy (REBT). I employ a structure of treatment that I have developed, inspired by the pioneering work of American psychotherapist Albert Ellis, enabling patients to achieve emotional responsibility.

It is my hope that this booklet will help more people to stop smoking as well as being of assistance to other therapists and hypnotherapy students.

● This book is divided into three sections, and I suspect it is to the second section, which provides instructions on self-hypnosis, that many readers will be tempted to turn first. I would urge you, however, to read and understand the reasoning and principles contained in the first section before moving on. Once these principles have been grasped you will be able to integrate them into your unconscious through self-hypnosis.

● If you are presenting any psychiatric disorders or suffering from clinical depression, it is advisable that you receive treatment for such conditions prior to embarking on becoming a non-smoker using this text.

Section One

CHAPTER ONE
Hypnosis & smoking cessation

If you have bought this book, there is a good chance you're a smoker.

It may be you have been smoking for a long time and perhaps have tried to stop on previous occasions.

But it hasn't worked.

Now you hope hypnotherapy could provide the answer?

Perhaps this treatment has been recommended by a friend, a colleague, or by a relative.

Even so, you might still feel wary?

If that's the case, don't worry; I meet a lot of people who before they come to see me have some strange ideas about hypnosis. I hope, though, that by the time you finish reading this book, you will come to see the practice in a positive light and, more importantly, understand just how easy it is to become a non-smoker using the programme detailed in these pages.

For those of you who intend to seek the help of a professional practitioner in person, I would say it is in your interest to know that a single session of properly administered clinical hypnosis is all it should take to successfully treat someone who has made the decision to quit.

So, how does hypnosis work?

First of all, it's important to make clear that hypnosis is not something to be worried about – in fact, it's a relaxing and motivating experience.

And when a client leaves my clinic after treatment he or she does so as a non-smoker, able to get on with the rest of his or her life unburdened by a "dependency" on cigarettes.

And that's a euphoric feeling.

The realisation that at last YOU are free from the enslavement of nicotine is going to be exhilarating.

During trance, clients are able to address issues buried deep within their subconscious as the practitioner helps them to work through various issues.

Treatment challenges people's long-held beliefs, allowing them to recognise that they don't actually need – or want – to smoke.

No longer will you feel anxious about feeding your "addiction" – anxious about the irrevocable damage being caused to your health; no longer troubled about how you are going to find the cash to pay for cigarettes. Nor will you be anxious about how others might perceive your dependency.

Psychologically, smokers who quit feel able to cope with life's stresses much more effectively without cigarettes, even if at this point you believe this to be far from the truth. The reality is that the smoker who quits is no longer held back by the demands of cigarettes.

And that ex-smoker can be you.

As someone who has quit, you become part of the non-smoking community, which is a status that most likely you have been aspiring to for years.

It is likely that you have yearned to be able to one day call yourself a non-smoker.

Cognitive behavioural hypnotherapy refers to such yearnings as '**healthy envy**'.

It might be useful to expand a little on that term because envy is a word usually associated with negative issues. But there is such a thing as healthy envy – it enables us to make positive changes in our lives.

There is also '**unhealthy envy**'.

For example, there are individuals who may hold an unhealthy envy of friends who have managed to stop smoking.

"How come my friend gave up so easily but I find it so hard?"

Such a sentiment can make an individual feel inadequate. The smoker with unhealthy envy may even try to jeopardise what their friend has achieved by urging him or her to start smoking again – perhaps offering the friend a cigarette at every opportunity.

On the other hand, the person who is still a smoker might experience healthy envy. I meet many such people in my consulting room – people who have come to see me on the recommendation of someone I have treated previously.

Their view is that while they envy the friend who has stopped smoking they feel that with a little help they might be able to achieve the same thing.

And I tell them that, of course, they can.

Immediately after treatment, that person will recognise he or she is a non-smoker – just like their friend and just like all the other untroubled non-smokers they know.

So just to reiterate: there exists healthy envy and unhealthy envy.

As you progress through these pages, you will notice that the terms healthy and unhealthy negative emotions or healthy and unhealthy beliefs are referred to quite frequently. I use the descriptions in a psychological sense; as you distinguish the difference between related emotions, so you will grasp how easy it is to stop smoking.

At this stage, I feel it might be useful to briefly outline the structure of this book – a sort of quick guide to successful treatment, which you might wish to refer back to now and again as you progress through the chapters.

If at this stage you find that you don't grasp some of the points, don't worry – all should become clear soon enough.

Your quick guide to quitting

1. Recognise and decide that you need and want to stop smoking. You are taking responsibility.
2. If you wish, list all the negative aspects of smoking and also all the positive aspects of not being a smoker. This can help emphasise the logic of your decision to stop.
3. You need to understand what your condition is. Smoking is an addiction of both body and mind but the physical demands are very short-lived and are easily overcome. It is the psychological element of smoking that is the primary issue.

4. Once you understand "The Power of Now" you will realise that your physical dependency can be broken instantly. Once you have determined that you are a non-smoker you become one with immediate effect – there is no qualifying period.

5. Once you have accepted that what you once thought of as physical dependency is actually a psychological issue you will understand that it is your fear of not being able to cope without cigarettes that has deceived you. It is this fear that manifests itself in anxiety. And this anxiety is what you have previously misinterpreted as being physical withdrawal symptoms.

6. Your fear is a conditioned response. It is an unhealthy negative emotion. But you can change this. You take emotional responsibility.

7. You have nothing to fear. Intrusive thoughts are nothing to fear. You will learn not to be afraid of them.

8. Embrace your new understanding of the smoker's condition. For many of you, this book will provide you with enough insight to stop or, with the help of a clinical hypnotherapist, your new-found comprehension can be integrated into your unconscious through trance; self-hypnosis can also work and I have included an

explanation of this exercise in Section Two of this book.

9. Enjoy the freedom of no longer being a smoker; enjoy the freedom of no longer using life events as an excuse to smoke.
10. Let others know how easy it is to stop.

CHAPTER TWO
The fear of fear

For most smokers, the biggest hurdle to stopping is actually taking the decision to do so. You know that you want to stop but you have asked yourself so many times when the best time will be to do so.

It is likely you have already postponed the "dreaded day" numerous times.

But you are not alone. I guess there are millions of smokers who genuinely want to stop yet when it comes to the crunch they are always able to trawl up an excuse to postpone doing so.

Of course, there are countless excuses for delay but in reality there is really only one reason smokers find it hard to quit.

And that reason is **FEAR**.

I know that a lot of people will be reluctant to hear that statement and some will dismiss the notion as nonsense or they might even be angered by it.

So, I need to explain.

Smokers are fearful of the hardships that they believe lie ahead once they give up cigarettes.

They are scared about how they are going to cope.

They are worried about how they won't be able to stop thinking about cigarettes.

All these intrusive thoughts seem overwhelming.

Already the smoker is beginning to panic. (*See appendix: Panic*).

But stopping smoking really doesn't have to be at all difficult.

Treatment at my clinic begins by recognising that smoking is both a physical and psychological practice.

But most people confuse the two.

Such confusion is not that surprising, though, the reason being that nicotine addiction manages to disguise itself so well.

The physical aspect of nicotine addiction is actually overcome very quickly, despite what so many people have been led to believe over the years.

This physical aspect actually plays only a minor role in the habit and it is easily conquered as is explained as this book progresses.

It is the psychological aspect of smoking that presents the more challenging obstacle.

But this psychological aspect need not be hard to overcome.

And this is the purpose of these chapters – to explain why giving up smoking can be easy.

Stop smoking – it's a doddle.

It's a simple message.

Of course, that's a claim that is bound to raise a few eyebrows – the accepted view being, as I've said already, that trying to kick the habit is a massive, daunting challenge.

I hear that all the time from people I have yet to help.

And it is what so many people genuinely believe.

But it is simply NOT true.

It is a myth.

It need not be daunting at all.

CHAPTER THREE
Mistakes & misunderstanding

At my clinic, I have successfully treated a large number of smokers over the years.

When they have first come to me there has been hardly one who has not had some tale of woe to tell me about the tribulations of earlier attempts to quit.

"I bit my fingers to the bone."

"No-one dare come near me, I was that wound-up."

"I'd sit in a room with the light off and clench my fists so tightly I could see the white of my knuckles in the dark."

That last one might have been overstating matters a bit but I appreciate the image.

The following sentiment is a more common one:

"I put on three stone in weight because I was snacking so much just to take my mind off having a fag. And after all that, I ended up back on them."

Those are just a few examples of the kind of stories related by people who had already tried to stop smoking on at least one occasion before they decided to seek my help.

Some had also tried e-cigarettes only to return to smoking.

The comments of these people indicate to me that they have tackled the issue wrongly. In particular, those individuals who put on weight when trying to give up smoking have misunderstood their condition. They have tried to curb self-inflicted cravings with a substitute – and that substitute has been food.

If you have ever tried previously to stop smoking and ended up a few sizes larger, then it is not surprising that you might be sceptical of someone like myself claiming that cutting out cigarettes is going to be a doddle.

It is my job, though, to convince you that what I am saying is correct.

As you read on, you will understand how cravings are eradicated through hypnotherapy.

However, I don't doubt that every smoker who relates to me a tale of torment about quitting is telling me the truth; I acknowledge that such people have indeed suffered. And I sympathise with each and every one of them. Their problem has been that they have failed to recognise the true nature of smoking. Yet this is excusable for now – as I have said, the addiction disguises itself well. Once you understand, this excuse will no longer be acceptable, of course.

It is the FEAR of giving up that has been the problem.

At my clinic the FEAR of giving up is treated by regarding the emotion as an obsession that in turn has become a compulsion. (I have to state, though, that smoking is not medically diagnosed as an OCD – that being an obsessive compulsive disorder. However, I do employ some of the same techniques to help smokers quit as I would in the treatment of an OCD. Some professionals might counter that this is a misrepresentation of the definition of an OCD but I disagree. However, rather than dwell on the matter at this stage, I have included an expanded explanation of my reasoning in the appendix. (*See appendix: Obsessive Compulsive Disorders*)

CHAPTER FOUR
Coughers fill the coffers

Most smokers I meet admit quite candidly that they regret the day they ever lit up for the first time.

I am tempted to go further and say that EVERY smoker, at some time or other, regrets the day that he or she lit up that first cigarette.

I am using the word "day" quite deliberately – this being because smoking can hook people just like that… one day you inhale on a cigarette out of curiosity and before you know it you have been reeled in and the tobacco bosses are rubbing their hands in glee. This should be of no surprise as these people have much to celebrate… they have landed yet another unsuspecting recruit. The new smoker is worth tens of thousands of pounds to them, it being the coughers who fill their coffers.

It's a sad fact that more people worldwide smoke now than ever before and tobacco use still kills more than six million every year. Health experts estimate that cigarettes will claim 10 million lives each year up to 2030, of which seven million will be in the developing world.

But you have the chance and the choice not to be among such startling statistics.

And I don't for a minute doubt that if smokers are honest with themselves, most will admit that they really DO want to stop.

If you are still reading this, you have most likely already arrived at this conclusion.

Deep down, I am sure, you are desperate to quit.

Yet, there remain many smokers who find it hard to admit that they really do want to stop – these people insist that they continue to smoke out of choice.

Smokers dread the supposed torment that they believe lies ahead. They are terrified by the thought of getting through a single day without the psychological crutch of a cigarette – in other words they are scared of being unable to cope.

Their feelings can be summed up by that one key word again: FEAR.

They conclude that it is futile even to think of stopping as they are so scared that they are going to fail. And so they tell themselves that the time is not yet quite right to give up.

They have a FEAR of failure.

There are also a few smokers – a small minority, I would be willing to wager – who insist very strongly that they actually do not want to stop. Understandably, I have not seen many of them at my clinic but I have overheard them in casual conservations elsewhere.

"I like it too much."

OR

"No-one's going to tell me what I can do."

OR

"What's the point – you're going to die of something, anyway."

The reality is that all these sentiments are little more than defensive bravado – excuses being made by people reluctant to admit to themselves that they are more scared by the thought of giving up than they are of the consequences of continuing.

They prefer to ignore or disbelieve the perils of smoking or possibly they convince themselves that they will be one of those fabled smokers still puffing away defiantly at some grand old age.

Statistics do not support such optimism but people are all too often reluctant to acknowledge reality.

I always ask any smoker who arrives at my clinic if they are sure they are ready to stop.

If they are unsure, I suggest politely that they go away and come back to see me when they have changed their mind.

There have also been some smokers who have sought my help having reasoned that they need to stop smoking because it is holding them back or preventing them from achieving their dreams. Their mantra has become that if it wasn't for cigarettes they'd have been picked for the first team or had enough money to set up their own business etc. My response is to tell them to stop blaming cigarettes for their fear of under-achieving. Again it's a case of: taking responsibility. Stop being scared – stop smoking and have a go at reaching your goals.

The sooner any smoker comes to the conclusion that he or she needs to stop, the better. But it is not my job to sit in judgment – I am simply trying to be of assistance and when a smoker finally grasps responsibility and decides it is time to stop, then, I will help that person succeed.

I'm aware that it is all too easy to find excuses for putting off the day you quit. I'm also aware of how the days can become weeks and the weeks become months and the months become years.

It is a simple matter of accepting responsibility. The sooner you quit, the better.

CHAPTER FIVE
Times have changed

I do concede that smokers have a right to smoke if that is what they want to do – or more accurately if that is what they mistakenly believe that they want to do.

It is only fair, though, that they in turn respect the right of other people not to have to breathe in their fumes.

Happily, I think nowadays that most smokers do respect the rights of the non-smoker.

It is not so long ago, though, that it was normal for people to light up more or less anywhere they wanted and, more often than not, that included most workplaces.

In an office, for example, someone who did not smoke could be sitting next to someone with a 20 or 30-a-day habit. The usual response to any protest was for the non-smoker to be told to find a desk elsewhere (or words to that effect.)

Smokers defended their right to light up and any demands not to do so were met with vociferous accusations of their personal freedoms being infringed.

Times have changed, though.

Nowadays, millions of us are no longer subjected to passive smoking – we are no longer the victims of other people's overriding wishes on this issue.

While there might still be the odd grumbling about "non-smoking fascists," most smokers nowadays seem to accept that others have the right not to share their habit.

Of course, you are bound to moan a bit when, rather than being indoors in the warmth, you try to light up a cigarette in the wind and rain. As you shiver on the office doorstep or in some designated smoking area, it might be a good time to ask yourself why you suffer such misery and indignity.

Little wonder that the habit leaves so many smokers with a sense of guilt, humiliation, or shame – all "unhealthy negative emotions".

CHAPTER SIX
Victims of a massive con

In the previous chapter, I mentioned some of the many negative aspects of smoking, including the indignities suffered by smokers.

So, why do they do it?
Or if you happen to be one of them: why do YOU do it?

Well, to my mind, one of the major reasons people smoke is that they are victims.

Smokers are victims of a huge conspiracy – a massive con trick.

And, of course, they have every reason to be upset by this.

Few people like the idea of being perceived a victim but acknowledging this fact and letting go of pride is useful in opening the door to giving up.

If you are a smoker, your health has become a victim of the corporate pursuit of profit.

So, I would say very strongly that it is time to take back control. The thought that someone else is getting rich by your exploitation is not a pleasant one.

I know that a lot of smokers are reluctant to see themselves as victims, of course. It makes them feel weak or at best uncomfortable.

It is easier for them to insist that they smoke out of choice.

I might at this stage point out that I do not consider smokers weak-willed individuals. I do believe, though, that smokers are deluded – that they are encouraged to think that their habit is one of choice.

Just a little earlier, I cited the smoker who says something along the lines of: "No-one's going to tell me what I can do."

It is the defence of the smoker who resents being advised to quit.

It is just as valid to point out that no-one has the right to insist that he does smoke, either.

Of course, he might not believe that he is being manipulated and continue to insist that his smoking is a matter of personal choice.

Tobacco companies, of course, support this view of free will and are content to contend that it is a person's right to choose whether or not they smoke.

There are organisations that add credence to this claim. There are several tobacco related agencies, directly funded or supported by the tobacco industry; including Freedom Organisation for the Right to Enjoy Smoking Tobacco (FOREST). The group's prime claim is to preserve the right of individual choice, in particular the right to smoke. There is also a Tobacco Retailer's Alliance which operates on behalf of tobacco retailers and others associated with the industry.

It is not hard to see why tobacco industry executives support this assertion of free will: it helps them maintain their grip on the smoking population. After all, they have spent a lot of time and money establishing their dominance and are less than willing to give that up without a fight.

It puts them in a more comfortable position to deflect away from themselves any blame for people's smoking habits.

And so instead, they insist that people are free to make their own decisions – that they, the tobacco companies, are there merely to service a public demand.

Your best response is to recognise that you are free to give up.

Why be a victim?

In my view, smoking is one of the biggest confidence tricks in history and has wreaked appalling consequences over many years.
It bemuses me that the concept of smoking ever caught on.

But catch on it did and almost before you could say: "Pass me the ashtray" it became fashionable to smoke.

It is well documented that Hollywood played a huge role in providing smokers with kudos—movie stars heroically inhaling their way to early graves. Cigarette endorsement (when a major star was seen to be smoking) fast became the preferred method for cigarette companies to influence movie goers to develop desirable associations between their cinema idols and cigarettes (*Sargent et al.*)

But those cinema greats were victims, too – craggy-faced icons such as Humphrey Bogart. And then there were the female actors who persuaded the world that women should be equally free to smoke and thereby unwittingly helped swell corporate wallets to bursting point.

And there was the relentless advertising, too – a major weapon in the arsenal of the cigarette industry. Publicity started way back with magazine ads in the 19th century in such publications as Punch. Cigarette cards were also prevalent from 1875, depicting actors and sports stars. And so tobacco advertising grew.

It is easy to forget that it is only relatively recently that governments have taken any convincing steps to address the issue.

The cigarette companies might plead that they try only to promote branding to those who already smoke. My observation is that they will go as far as they are permitted in order to lure people into addiction. In countries where advertising cigarettes is still legal, the tobacco firms continue to do so with abandon. And more than 130 countries have minimal or no policies covering the use of warning labels on cigarette packaging.

But smokers are not victims of just the tobacco giants. They are victims of the huge misconception that giving up smoking is one of the hardest things in the world to achieve. And that misconception invokes fear.

The idea that giving up smoking is tough has evolved over the decades to such an extent that it is now deeply entrenched.

And for that reason I am not surprised that people might mock my insistence that quitting need not be hard.

I accept that it is a valid question to ask that if my assertion is correct, why is it that the opposite view has prevailed so long?

Part of the answer is that when an idea becomes so established, as it has done regarding the physical addictive nature of tobacco, it becomes self-fulfilling – in other words a person presumes it is going to be tough to stop smoking and, as a result, tough it does indeed become.

This is anxiety feeding anxiety – a self-fulfilling prophesy.

It might be helpful to point out who is responsible for establishing and maintaining this myth about smoking – simply with a view to helping debunk the falsehood.

The tobacco bosses, I've already listed – they have a financial stake in people continuing to buy cigarettes. Theirs is a detached, business stance motivated by profit. If it were possible to manufacture a totally harmless cigarette they would presumably lend it their support for cold, commercial reasons – the longer smokers survive, the longer they are going to be around to buy tobacco products. The involvement of tobacco companies in the expansion of e-cigarette sales should, perhaps, be of little surprise.

But who else is it that nurtures the myth that stopping smoking is so tough?

Fellow smokers come high up that list.

I mentioned the unhealthy envy of some smokers a little earlier. Such smokers can be quick to discourage others trying to quit, undermining their endeavours at any opportunity. It is an "unhealthy negative emotion".

Such action also stems from a misguided trust in the notion of there being safety in numbers. People take comfort in numbers – usually the larger the number the better – the thinking being that the more people who participate in a particular pursuit or habit, the more acceptable is that action.

Smokers perpetuate the myth of it being difficult to stop, not just to excuse what they perceive to be their own failings but also to maintain their numbers by dissuading others from leaving their ranks.

Even some of those who have successfully deserted the smokers' army and joined the legions of ex-smokers promote the myth – managing to quit against the odds being regarded as somehow more heroic than success having been really rather easy.

I recognise, of course, that for many ex-smokers, stopping was indeed a gruelling ordeal meriting a medal of the highest order (but it was tough only because the smoker believed the myths surrounding cessation).

Ironically, others who also perpetuate the myth about it being hard to quit include some organisations and individuals that actively campaign against smoking.

They may be doctors, counsellors and therapists or other health workers of one kind or another, including, some hypnotherapists.

I am not suggesting that the intentions of any such people are anything but sincere or honourable; it is simply my contention that smoking should be treated primarily as a psychological disorder.

I have already stated that I treat smoking as I would an obsession that has led to the compulsion to smoke.

CHAPTER SEVEN
Substitutes

Hopefully, I've left no-one in doubt of my assertion that smoking is primarily a psychological disorder.

Most treatments you are likely to be offered, however, are based on the assumption that smoking is principally a physical addiction and this strengthens the presumption that giving up is going to be a prolonged and uphill battle. The likelihood of relapse, in this case, also increases.

You will more than likely be familiar with at least some of the various devices and tobacco substitutes available and I have already mentioned e-cigarettes.

Popular as these devices and substitutes might have become, it is a fact that they not only fail to overcome physical addiction but also reinforce the myth that quitting is one big challenge.

When clients come to me wanting to stop, I discourage them from using such replacements. More often than not, they will have already tried to stop with the assistance of such products but been unsuccessful.

Chewing nicotine gum, for example, is still putting a poison into the body; I agree that it is far less harmful to ingest nicotine than to inhale it because one is no longer taking in a myriad of the other poisonous chemicals contained in tobacco smoke. But ultimately, the physical addiction is being sustained without the psychosomatic habit being overcome. One consequence of this is that the incidence of relapse is high. In other words, the smoker has suppressed the habit temporarily rather than abandoned it.

Nicotine patches are another product of pharmacotherapy and I would contend the success rate is hardly impressive and in a percentage of those cases, success is a result of the placebo effect *(See appendix: placebo effect)* – in other words, their application is psychologically effective rather than physically effective.

To my mind, the necessity of eliminating the drug that has caused the addiction in the first place seems fairly obvious.

I have listened to clients at my clinic who had tried e-cigarettes as a substitute but had then gone back to smoking tobacco before eventually coming to see me. They believed that their reversion was a demonstration of how strong their physical addiction to tobacco was.

But that's not true.

In fact, it demonstrates the opposite.

If the smokers' addiction was primarily physical, then e-cigarettes would have broken their habit and the client would have stopped because the e-cigarette was delivering nicotine into the body, and thereby satisfying the physical urge. The fact that ultimately the e-cigarettes had failed to break the habit is evidence, therefore, that the addiction is indeed a psychological one.

According to a report by the BBC in September 2013 and results published in the Lancet, 7.3 per cent of people using e-cigarettes had quit smoking after six months. Prof Peter Hajek, director of Tobacco Dependency Research at Queen Mary University, London, called for more long-term studies into the consequences of using the devices. In America the University of California's Centre for Tobacco Research and Education stated its studies (published in 2014) had found that using e-cigarettes was associated with an increased likelihood of experimentation with conventional cigarettes. The study was conducted among American adolescents and it added that results "suggest that e-cigarette use is aggravating rather than ameliorating the tobacco epidemic among youths".

In 2015, publication of research at Johns Hopkins University, Maryland, USA, suggested that vapour produced by e-cigarettes

31

compromised the immune system in the lungs, leaving them more vulnerable to infection.

Doubtless, there will be organisations and individuals who are going to be contending statistics and research for years to come.

My own opinion is that, preferable though e-cigarettes might be in comparison to smoking conventional cigarettes, it is still unwise to suggest that e-cigarettes are harmless.

I am also unhappy by the manner in which statistics have at times been misrepresented in some circles to suggest e-cigarettes are far more successful in helping people stop smoking than is actually the case.

The cost of these tobacco substitutes should also not be forgotten.

My main contention, though, remains that cigarette-substitutes help to perpetuate the myth of nicotine "dependency".

The treatment that I offer is, as I keep emphasising, based on the principle that smoking is primarily a psychological rather than a physical problem and can be easily overcome.

I don't claim to be the first person to make such a pronouncement – one pioneer was Allen Carr whose book The Easy Way to Stop Smoking has helped thousands of smokers to quit.

I am in agreement with the fundamental principles of Carr's argument, though I would add that hypnotherapy is able to integrate positive principles into the unconscious mind.

In his book, Carr, who was a 100-a-day smoker before giving up, stated that he finally quit after consulting a hypnotherapist.

An important element of the treatment I offer is the acceptance of self-efficacy – that is a person's belief in his or her ability to achieve goals.

This concept of self-efficacy – having a belief in one's ability to succeed in a particular situation – was explored in studies by leading American/Canadian psychologist Albert Bandura. *(See appendix: Self-efficacy)*

Sadly, the myth peddled about the difficulties facing smokers striving to quit has shattered many people's self-efficacy – in other words, they have been influenced by others.

Observing how others deal with situations can have a powerfully negative impact on self-efficacy. Being placed in a class of well behaved, conscientious pupils, for example, will reinforce a child's own belief of his self-efficacy through his classmates' successes. In contrast, a child placed in a class of unruly children is likely to have lower self-belief in his or her ability to attain high achievement.

The accepted notion concerning cigarettes is that giving up is harrowing at best and in most cases doomed to failure. Were this not the case, why would so many Nicotine Replacement Therapy (NRT) products exist? Confidence concerning quitting smoking has been constantly shaken by NRT marketing reinforcing the myth that quitting smoking is a painful process. Society has been swayed by the collective negative "voice" of thousands of failed quitters. This message is absorbed into the subconscious, creating a fear of quitting.

The failure of most of the smoking cessation programmes, including NRT treatments, most likely seems to be due to neglecting to include self-efficacy as an imperative factor motivating smokers to quit.(*Martinez et al.*)

Happily, hypnotherapy is able to help people develop a strong sense of self efficacy and motivation. It might be encouraging for readers to know that over the past few years I have successfully treated hundreds of clients who have sought my help to stop smoking.

One other point I feel ethically obliged to point out, having already mentioned the high cost of cigarette substitutes, is that I do charge a fee for helping people to stop smoking (my rates are available on my clinic's website). These fees, of course, help provide me with a livelihood but importantly for the smoker, they also impose a sacrifice that helps focus his or her mind and encourages him or her to grasp responsibility.

The good news for many people is that they will be able to quit smoking simply by understanding and adhering to the principles I am endeavouring to explain in this book and as a result will not need to seek further help. If you are one such person – you can treat this little book as you might a DIY manual and in doing so save yourself some money. Please practise the self-hypnosis tasks in Section Two of this book if you are committed to stop smoking. If you follow the guidance each day, for three weeks then it will become a doddle to stop.

For those who do seek the direct assistance of a hypnotherapist, I would recommend that it is worth determining that your practitioner is suitably trained and qualified. Being a member of the British Society of Clinical Hypnosis (BSCH) myself, my recommendation, as you might expect, is that you ensure that any practitioner in the UK whom you consult is also a member of the society, as the BSCH demands its members adhere to a strict code of practice. *(See appendix: British Society of Clinical Hypnosis, BSCH)*

And it is worth recalling that, as I state in the opening chapter of this book, a single session of properly administered clinical hypnosis is all it should take to treat successfully someone who has made the decision to quit.

CHAPTER EIGHT
What to expect

Part of my rationale for saying that it is easy to stop smoking is based, as I outlined earlier, on my understanding that the fear of not smoking can be treated as a therapist would treat an obsession and compulsion.

So exactly what role can hypnotherapy play?
What can smokers seeking to stop expect when they come to my clinic?

It might be useful to give a brief, general insight into hypnotherapy, and dispel any common misconceptions about its practice.

Firstly, clinical hypnosis should not be confused with stage hypnosis, which you might have encountered on a night out, or on TV shows.

Stage hypnosis is performed by entertainers. When they allegedly hypnotise a subject on television or in front of an audience they are actually indulging in mind manipulation – that is, bending the particular subject's will to adhere to authority. And that is not how I would define hypnosis. Suspecting that this statement might be controversial or even unpopular, I have included an expanded explanation in the appendix of this booklet. *(See appendix: Stage hypnosis)*

Few reputable clinical hypnotherapists will use his or her skills for the amusement of an audience. I am not condemning stage "hypnotism", simply arguing that it should be seen for what it is: entertainment and illusion. In the appendix, I reveal some of the methods employed by entertainers and point out how such techniques are sometimes used in other fields to influence people – by politicians, for example.

Clinical hypnotherapy sessions, on the other hand, are designed to help people seeking treatment for a variety of issues – and one of these issues is smoking.

CHAPTER NINE
The Unconscious

Hypnotism deals with the unconscious. It is worth recognising that our very survival depends on the unconscious.

Sometimes, though, the very same functions we rely upon can prove a threat to our well-being when certain 'alien' factors, (such as smoking), are introduced.

Our unconscious, for example, allows us to be optimistic – we need a degree of optimism to get us through the hard times in our lives.

It means that when presented with certain outcomes we prefer to imagine the more favourable scenario. In some situations such a preference can give us an advantage.

But for smokers, when they think of the consequences of their actions, they invariably prefer to think of some 100-year-old who has smoked a packet or more a day since childhood with no ill effects. I have yet to meet any such individual.

Our tendency is to minimise life's negatives and emphasise its positives. The trouble with smoking is that it is nothing but negative.

During a trance, the therapist will put the patient's unconscious back in touch with reality.

The treatment will include some **negative reinforcement**. But negative reinforcement is only a part of the package.

You do not need to be in a trance to list the negative points of smoking but the hypnotherapist will bring those aspects into clear focus. (I deal more fully with negative reinforcement in Section Two.)

It would be a useful exercise for anyone intending to stop smoking without the help of a hypnotherapist to make his or her own list about the negative impact of smoking.

It is not my intention to labour this point, however, because I am of the view that being nagged about it is unlikely to be helpful. In fact, nagging raises **anxiety** which for smokers means they are more likely than ever to feel in need of a cigarette (though there is a good chance that before coming to the clinic they have been oblivious to the fact that cigarettes actually raise a person's vulnerability to anxiety.)

Dwelling on the physical consequences of smoking can also heighten a smoker's anxiety and once again **deceive** the smoker into feeling the need to reach for the packet of cigarettes.

For the ex-smoker, though, reflecting from time to time on the ills that he or she has left behind can be a useful and strengthening exercise.

And that is why, during clinical hypnosis at my surgery, the client is subjected to a degree of negative reinforcement. A variety of techniques are explained in Section Two.

When treatment is finished, the client leaves the clinic as a NON-SMOKER, happy to be no longer bound to a drug that has been causing him or her so much harm.

Hypnosis is not magic but it is able to turn "switches" on and off – metaphorically – and therefore the individual is able to accept that he or she might once have been a smoker but, after coming out of a trance, that is a part of his or her life that he or she is happy to have left behind.

That individual is a non-smoker.

There is no qualifying time to becoming a non-smoker; it isn't a case of you becoming a non-smoker after a week, or after a month, or after a year of having that last cigarette. Once out of trance the threshold has already been crossed.

You are now, with immediate effect, a non-smoker. *(See appendix: Power of Now)*

Ex-smokers no longer have to live with any feeling of guilt about the illnesses they might be

41

inviting into their bodies; they need no longer suffer the knowledge that such ill health would be self-inflicted; they no longer need to distress themselves about the adverse effect their addiction is having on the lives of all those other people who love them and care for their well-being.

For some, the most important aspect of being a non-smoker is no longer having to suffer the perceived humiliation of being a smoker.

The smoker who quits is able to regain self-respect.

It seems almost churlish to mention some of the other more trivial benefits of not smoking but to many people they are not insignificant: ex-smokers can be confident that the smell of stale smoke on their breath and clothes is a thing of the past.

The person who stops smoking also abandons the rigours that his or her addiction imposes on the ageing process, in particular the dry and wrinkled facial skin, evident on many long-term smokers.

And then there is the money the ex-smoker is saving. There can be few smokers unaware that smoking is hitting them hard in the pocket – and the cost has been rising dramatically in recent years.

The fact that a smoker is prepared to continue to pay exorbitant prices is a reflection of the psychological hold exercised by cigarettes. Smokers will still light up despite the knowledge that, in effect, they are burning money. They might try to cut the cost by buying contraband cigarettes but consumer reports indicate that these are all too often more lethal even than the legal brands.

In many instances, smokers are willing to forgo not only small pleasures but necessities, such as food, to sustain their habit.

Feel free to add any more personal negatives – personal negatives that you will be glad to abandon.

The main fact is that everything about smoking is negative.

There are no positives.

CHAPTER TEN
Vulnerability

I have just stated there are no positive aspects to smoking.

It is at this stage that some smokers reading this book might raise a firm, if wheezy, objection. They might concede that while there are certainly some negatives about their habit there are nevertheless a few obvious positive aspects to smoking that I am choosing to deliberately ignore.

But they are deluded.

I can appreciate why the claim might be made but such an assertion is wrong and smokers who cite alleged advantages have mistaken the true nature of their addiction.

The so-called "pleasures" that smokers might refer to are delusory. The mind as well as the body is being manipulated.

Please don't think I am sitting in moral judgment of anyone by making these statements; I just look and analyse behaviour and when that behaviour is harmful, I am able to help that person move in another, positive direction.

Smokers just happen to have had the misfortune of having been exposed to smoking at some vulnerable point in their life and have picked up the habit as a result... or let me be emphatic – they consider themselves biological addicts as a result.

The most likely time for a person to take up smoking is a period in their lives when they are susceptible – a time when they are most likely to be influenced by peer pressure; a time when they are eager to fit in, to conform; a time when they are reluctant to seem different.

Most of us go through such a stage or stages to varying degrees at some time in our lives, most often during adolescence and it is no coincidence that it is as teenagers that most smokers start their habit.

And, just for the record, that makes it all the more inexcusable that cigarette manufacturers might make their products in any way appealing to young people. The allure can be subtle – packaging is particularly tempting, a powerful marketing weapon.

And if it helps make cigarettes seem "cool" then it is going to attract youngsters.

But it is not just teenagers who smoke. Smokers include among their numbers people of different ages and from all different kinds of backgrounds.

I am aware, for example, that there are plenty of men and women who are smokers who might also be regarded, by the values of the consumer society, as rich and successful. I would contend, though, that there are very few of them who have taken up the habit since becoming rich and successful adults. It is more than likely that they fell under the spell of cigarettes at a time in their lives when they were more easily influenced by others.

And now they feel that they cannot do without their cigarettes – they are still being influenced.

Of course, they understand it would be beneficial to give up smoking but they have convinced themselves that they have numerous reasons for not doing so.

Again the pack mentality comes into play and it is comforting for them to know there are others who share their habit. They jolly each other along, reassuring one another that they smoke because they wish to. They believe that to admit otherwise would be a sign of weakness.

Yet, they are gripped by fear at the thought of trying to cope without cigarettes.

It is easier for them to pretend to others that they are untroubled by their habit or if you like, that they don't give a damn.

Deep down, though, they know, as I know, that they DO give a damn.

It's just that they feel it convenient to simply postpone the day that they will give up.

But when will that day ever come?

It is time to take responsibility.

Make the decision that you have to quit and once that is determined you have cleared that first but highest hurdle.

For some, the awareness that it is time to accept personal responsibility comes easily – most women who become pregnant, for example, accept they have an obligation to care for themselves in order to care for the unborn child.

There are some smokers who intuitively grasp the concepts detailed in this book without reference to a professional therapist and give up smoking easily. It simply dawns on them that they do not need cigarettes. Their first step though will have been to recognise the need to stop and that they want to stop.

Whatever it is that prompts you into recognising that you really do need to stop, the important thing is for you to accept that fact.

My job is then to give you the tools to remove entirely your desire to smoke.

CHAPTER ELEVEN
Delusions

I have already referred to negative reinforcement and underlined the many harmful effects of smoking.

Now I want to dismantle the myths about the so-called "pleasures" of smoking before explaining the smoker's disorder.

I have already stated that what the smoker thinks of as "pleasure" is a delusion – a confidence trick.

If you are a smoker, however, you will probably believe – quite sincerely – that there are some benefits that smoking provides.

Here are the most common misconceptions:

"Cigarettes help against stress."

"They help me relax."

"They help me concentrate."

"They relieve boredom."

NO they don't.

It is all a delusion.
Nicotine is a stimulant.

Nicotine is also a poison and it affects your nervous system.

Once your body becomes acquainted with the drug – in other words once you are an addict – the body expects that level of nicotine to be maintained. When the levels begin to drop, a message is sent to the brain demanding a top-up. This is the agitation that the smoker feels when he or she has gone without a cigarette for half an hour or so. It is what you most likely call your craving.

"I'm dying for a fag!"

One or two puffs on a cigarette and the craving is gone – for the time being, at least – and the smoker is grateful for that cigarette.

The fact that the agitation was a result in the first place of being a smoker seems to be ignored by many.

Time after time after time, smokers go back to the object that is the cause of their aggravation.

They want that "fix".

A puff or two and they feel better.

But that initial gratification is ephemeral – it soon fades and before long the craving begins once more to reassert itself as the body's nicotine levels start to fall.

49

Here is an important fact for smokers to recognise: just as nicotine enters the body quickly, so it leaves the body quickly. Its physical hold on you, in other words, can be soon broken.

I will come back to this point presently.

To keep the body "topped up" equates on average to smoking about 20 cigarettes a day. It will vary according to circumstances throughout the day and the physical characteristics of the individual smoker.

There are, of course, a lot of smokers who smoke fewer cigarettes than 20 a day, though it is my observation that many smokers tend to underestimate the number of cigarettes they do smoke daily (this tendency to lie about their consumption might be seen as a covert admission that they recognise they should stop).

In some cases, people who smoke fewer cigarettes than 20 a day may suffer more than heavier-smoking colleagues. This is because they are addicts, just like the heavier smokers – if they were not they would stop – yet at the same time they are not satisfying their addiction. As a consequence, they can spend many of their waking hours in a state of agitation – much of each day spent looking forward to the time when they will allow themselves a smoke. Life can seem a constant battle. Their agitation can manifest itself in other symptoms, such as nail-biting, over-eating etc.

As for those smokers who for much of the day **genuinely** have no craving to smoke but feel the urge only in particular circumstances or at specific times – they are proof of the psychological nature of smoking. Their physical urge is triggered by the mind. They feel the need to smoke by association with a particular time or circumstance – perhaps when they have a coffee or are waiting for a bus or when their mind is no longer occupied by some distraction or absorbing activity such as work or a hobby.

But whether you are a heavy smoker or a light smoker... it makes no difference – it is the quelling of the agitation, which has been caused by the absence of nicotine that the smoker misinterprets as being a positive power. In other words, they are convinced that it is cigarettes that help them to relax, that it is cigarettes that help them to concentrate, that relieve boredom.

But it is all nonsense.

Take the notion that cigarettes help a person concentrate, for example.

No they don't.

Cigarettes are a constant distraction. The smoker is unable to concentrate for thinking about that next "fix".

It follows that once the fix has been administered, the smoker can concentrate and he or she is tempted to assume it is the cigarette that provides powers of concentration. What they perceive as being their heightened level of concentration lasts for the next twenty minutes or so when their concentration levels are in reality the same as those of a non-smoker. However, while the non-smoker continues to concentrate, the smoker is soon thinking about that next cigarette again and his or her concentration fades quickly. And so it goes on...and on...and on.

Similarly, the smoker likes to have his or her prop in social situations.

"It helps me relax, when I'm talking with people."

Nowadays, of course, fewer and fewer social occasions offer the opportunity to smoke. So the smoker seeking the chance to have a cigarette outside, or wherever, is actually being anti-social.

Their habit is seen by some as pitiful.

And the smoker may harbour feelings of guilt. Such emotions are hardly conducive to relaxation.

Once again, smoking is causing agitation and anxiety.

Smokers even worry about finding themselves in circumstances when they might be denied the opportunity to smoke and as a result they may restrict engagements to those times and places when they know they will be able to find a place to smoke. They may avoid long-haul flights or public transport; they may prefer to stay in their home rather than venturing out and meeting people.

I could carry on listing the misconceptions concerning the supposed therapeutic power of nicotine but hopefully I've been beating the drum loud enough already to get the message through:

Smoking is the cause not the cure of so many stressful situations.

• Studies into depression among smokers carried out at University College London, involving nearly 6,500 people aged over 40, prompted the following comment from Dr Mike Knapton, associate medical director at the British Heart Foundation which released the research findings: *"There is a belief from many smokers that smoking reduces anxiety and stress, which is in turn causing many smokers to put off quitting.*

"Yet instead of aiding people to relax, smoking increases anxiety and tension." (Report published in *i* newspaper 24/2/15).

CHAPTER TWELVE
Lifting the burden

One significant pleasure to look forward to as a non-smoker is the regaining of self-assurance. The constant, nagging doubt and the insecurity suffered by so many smokers is eradicated once the individual stops.

Many people I treat are surprised to discover what confident, capable people they really are once the burden of addiction has been lifted.

It has to be recognised, as I point out to clients, that there are still going to be times of anxiety and grief in one's life; there are still going to be stressful situations – situations that most of us have to face at some point or other.

This is just what happens in life.

But smoking is not going to relieve those stresses – quite the opposite.

It is non-smokers who are much better equipped to cope with the calamities and upsets that life inevitably throws at all of us.

Likewise, non-smokers are also much better equipped to enjoy the good things in life. Life's stresses should not be used as an excuse to smoke.

Some readers at this point might like to make a personal list of all the things they will enjoy again, or enjoy to a greater extent, once they have given up smoking.

It is useful to create and fix agreeable images in one's mind.

At the same time it might be a useful exercise to make a list of reasons why you have smoked. Recognise these are nothing but excuses rather than reasons and then tear up the list.

CHAPTER THIRTEEN
Weighty issues

Talking to many people who have quit smoking, I am aware there is one bonus that seems to be shared by the majority of ex-smokers and that is a heightened appreciation of food – and I am not meaning gluttony but a regaining of taste.

Listening to many smokers who come to see me, I hear that they rarely enjoy their meals properly – that they too often anticipate the cigarette that they intend to smoke once they finish eating.

Understandably, for some, the thought of not smoking raises the issue of weight gain.

It is a fear shared by many smokers that without cigarettes they are going to overeat to compensate for the absence of cigarettes in their lives and that therefore they will become fat.

It is true that many people who try to give up through sheer will power are often tempted to resort to food as a distraction from their "withdrawal" pangs.

They are using food as a tobacco substitute and as a consequence they overeat.

By doing so, they pile on the pounds – or, in some cases, the stones.

But under hypnosis, we deal with cravings. By eradicating perceived nicotine pangs, they are no longer a threat; the desire to use food as a substitute is removed.

This is reinforced with some of the same rational emotive behaviour principles that I employ when treating people who come for help solely about weight issues.

It might be useful for readers to recognise that there is a wide variety of problems that people suffer, all of which have common roots in the unconscious and that is why hypnosis can be such a radical force for good health and well-being and can, therefore, be employed to address such a large number of conditions.

Sometimes similar anxieties, stresses or worries will manifest themselves in different symptoms and disorders, depending on an individual's experience and character.

Returning, specifically, to the matter of smoking, as I stated earlier, I believe the fear people have of ceasing to smoke manifests symptoms that can be treated using the techniques detailed in this book.

I explain this to smokers who come to see me and I offer them treatment accordingly.

CHAPTER FOURTEEN
The placebo effect

After a client arrives at my clinic, there is an initial consultation session, which will usually last about an hour.

There are some people who come along and will say something along the lines of: *"Daniel, I've been smoking 40 cigarettes a day for 35 years and I'm a bit sceptical about how you're going to be able to turn me into a non-smoker in just one session. I've tried everything: patches, medicines, e-cigarettes – the lot. You name it, I've tried it. You're my last resort."*

There is then sometimes a pause and my client might add: *"I suppose it might work as a placebo or something; anyhow it's worth giving it a go."*

Their conclusion intrigues me. If their addiction is exclusively physical, why is it that nicotine patches or e-cigarettes, have failed? The pharmacotherapy provides nicotine and as such should boast a 100 per cent success rate if the addiction was purely physical.

Accordingly, on those occasions when a smoker does succeed in giving up while using substitutes it will be a result of the placebo effect, ie a belief that the product is going to be effective rather than the product in reality being medically effectual. In other words, success has been a psychological phenomenon.

In some cases, to be quite frank, it might be that hypnotherapy's success proves to be a result of the placebo effect – that is to say that there will be some people whose blind faith in the therapist will convince that person he or she is a non-smoker, rather than any understanding of the rationale behind the treatment.

Success, nevertheless, remains a psychological phenomenon. They are now a non-smoker and the fear they once held of becoming a non-smoker has been eradicated. They have been hypnotised.

CHAPTER FIFTEEN
Gaining insight

For my clients, the consultation is an important precursor to hypnosis itself and offers the client the opportunity to understand what exactly the treatment entails and how it works.

It also gives me the chance to discuss matters with the client and to get to know the person and learn about his or her smoking habits: is he the only smoker in his household, for example? Does she smoke because she thinks that otherwise she would be unable to cope with the demands of her job?

I take the opportunity to glean relevant details about the client's life – for example, are there young children in the family causing strain and tiredness?

Such knowledge helps me to tailor the treatment to the individual.

I consider each session a bespoke service designed to best suit the individual seeking help.

At the end of this consultation session, I allow the client time to decide if he or she wishes to proceed with full treatment, which involves being eased into a trance, assuming it is appropriate to do so.

At the end of the preliminary consultation session there are some clients who are under the impression that I have already completed the treatment, which is a good sign as it reflects how confident and motivated the client already feels about giving up smoking.

However, I have yet to guide them into a deep, focused hypnotic trance where healthy beliefs can be integrated into their unconscious.

During our consultation, I will have introduced the client to the subject of phobias. I do so because a phobia, such as the fear of not being able to smoke, is an irrational anxiety (an unhealthy negative emotion).

But you might be wondering why I don't simply address smoking issues directly?

It is because of the benefits that disassociation provides.

I am allowing clients to make the associations themselves and thus provide them with a vivid insight into their own behaviour. Just how quickly a client grasps this concept varies from person to person.

Hopefully, YOU are seeing that there is a difference between healthy beliefs and unhealthy beliefs.

Here is an example of a healthy negative emotion and an unhealthy negative emotion: **sadness** and **depression**.

There are times in life when we are going to feel sad. It is inevitable and it is natural. We might have suffered bereavement or it might just be that we have failed a driving test.

Sadness is natural and it is a HEALTHY negative emotion.

Depression is an UNHEALTHY negative emotion.

Individuals can put unsustainable pressure on themselves by refusing to accept disappointment and instead demand that everything MUST go their way.

People can hold unhealthy demands about any event and that emotion can last for seconds, minutes, hours, days, months or years.

Prolonged depression can trigger a chemical reaction where medication from a GP might be prescribed.

I will cite an example of an individual who suffers sadness, or it might be called short-term depression, after being made redundant from employment.

His reaction is: *"I can't believe this has happened to me; I don't think I'm going to be able to cope; I'm a failure; I've got no job."*

His response might then be to go to the pub and numb his feelings with alcohol or he might choose to lock himself away in his bedroom and have a cry.

Clearly, he is not happy about his redundancy but soon he manages to rationalise his predicament.

And then he can reason: *"OK, I wish it hadn't happened but I am going to cope. I have still got skills. I can find another job."*

The individual's attitudes have changed.

For some people, though, their attitude does not change and they remain in a depressed state, continuing to hold on to unhealthy demands.

In such a scenario, an individual might continue drinking every day and in turn feel a greater failure because of this behaviour which compounds his or her depression. He or she might then even hold the demand: "I MUST not be depressed."

They are now depressing themselves about depression.

CHAPTER SIXTEEN
Anxiety explained

When we are anxious our heart rates accelerate and we start to perspire and flush. People tense up. *(See appendix: anxiety and excitement)*

This is all perfectly normal.

I sometimes ask my clients: "What causes anxiety?"

They might reply: "Worry."

"Worry is another term for anxiety," I reply.

"Difficult situations," others will state.

We have already established that it is not these events that cause anxiety but our unhealthy, DEMANDING beliefs about them.

So, what does cause anxiety?

There are different theories.

One is that we are born with only a few anxieties, these being our **innate fears**: hunger and thirst, depth perception, loud, unexpected noises and scowling/snarling faces.

New-born babies cry when they are hungry and an adult will become very anxious if they themselves go without food or drink for too long.

Another innate fear is unexpected noises, especially loud ones. Unexpected, loud noises can shock, which causes our bodies to react with the natural symptoms of anxiety. The response is usually flight. We move away from the perceived danger.

Normal bodily functions change when our anxiety is heightened.

I now cite an imaginary example:

I slowly wave a pencil in front of a six-month-old baby.

The baby might show slight interest and his eyes will begin to follow the pencil. We then show the baby the same pencil and scream at the youngster and the baby will start to cry. Repeat the exercise over and over again and then all it will take to make the baby cry will be to show it the pencil without anyone having to scream. The baby's anxiety has been conditioned. (I would not, of course, condone anyone trying such a test which is clearly unethical – I cite it as a hypothetical example simply because it is an easy scenario for everyone to imagine as most of us are familiar to some extent with babies.)

I ask the client: is the baby scared of the pencil?

"No," they might reply or they might say: *"The baby's not scared of the pencil but is anticipating what's going to happen."*

Correct.

It is not the pencil that the baby fears, it is the noise – an innate fear.

Yet the noise has not occurred.

The baby starts to cry because he or she has become scared of becoming scared.

They are anxious about being anxious.

As the baby anticipates anxiety when seeing the pen, so the smoker anticipates anxiety when trying to quit. It is a conditioned response.

This theory implies that all anxiety except innate fear is self-fulfilling.

Nothing on this planet can cause us anxiety unless we allow ourselves to harbour fear.

Controversial this may be, but I believe this to be the case, my argument being that if it were not the case we could expect everyone's reaction to the same event to be identical and we all know that this is not so.

CHAPTER SEVENTEEN
Phobias

When I introduce the subject of phobias to clients, it is important that I select a phobia that does not actually afflict that particular person – I will have been careful to establish that this is the case already.

An example I like to use, where appropriate, refers to a phobia with which most people are familiar – the fear of spiders – arachnophobia.

It is likely that the person who does not have a phobia of spiders will nevertheless not be a particular fan of them either.

I now introduce what is known as a simple ABC model – devised by American psychotherapist Albert Ellis. It is a model with which psychology students are likely to be familiar and deals with distinguishing between healthy and unhealthy negative emotions.

A = Activating event
B = Beliefs
C = Consequences

The Consequences are the elements within the phobia – these being defined by the person's behaviour, their emotions, action tendencies (ie what the fearful person feels urged to do) plus the symptoms of their anxiety both in the mind and the body – the psychological and physiological.

Let's stick with the person whose phobia is spiders. They are scared of spiders, which is an irrational fear in the UK where spiders pose no danger. Even so, the phobia drives the sufferer into checking rooms to ensure there are no spiders lurking (behaviour); his or her anxiety (fear) is an ever-present emotion, manifesting itself in symptoms such as panic, sweating, nail biting, teeth grinding and if they are a smoker they might want a cigarette too; they feel they want to run away, to flee (action tendency) and they suffer intrusive thoughts, such as imagining spiders spinning webs beneath the bed.

Such intrusive thoughts can affect sleep.

I ask my client what he or she thinks might have caused the phobia. What has brought about this fear?

The most common response is to propose the idea that the phobia might be a consequence of something that has happened to them in the past.

They refer to a possible activating event that might have occurred or even an imaginary one, perhaps an incident in some tale they have been told as a youngster.

Events can be in the past, the present or they might be thoughts of the future.

I then explain how when a client comes to see me about a phobia of spiders they often tell me how a past real event has caused them to be anxious and how if they were to see a spider right there and then or in the future they would most certainly become anxious. Some say they would become hysterical.

However, we need to dispute the perceived cause of this fear.

Fear of spiders is not an innate fear. It is not a fear that any of us is born with.

If we were to ask 100 people if they suffer from a phobia of spiders the majority of them will say that while they might not be over fond of spiders, they don't have an actual phobia.

Yet among that majority will be people who have experienced the same activating event in their lives as a person who does have a phobia of spiders – perhaps they too saw a spider hanging from the ceiling over their bed as a young child?

But while one person has developed a phobia of spiders, the other person has not.

Their responses to that spider experience in earlier life have differed.

And this is the crux of the matter.

The phobia, the fear, the anxiety is not a result of an activating event.

That event, real or imagined, only APPEARS to be the cause.

But the phobia sufferer is convinced the activating event is the cause.

It is not that the activating event is irrelevant – past real events might have conditioned a response within that phobia-suffering individual and this has triggered the BELIEF which has become conditioned.

So…it is the BELIEF about any activating event that causes the CONSEQUENCE – it is the belief that causes the phobia, the obsession.

So, now we need to talk about these beliefs.

We know that there are two beliefs that an individual can hold about any activating event:

a HEALTHY BELIEF

or

an UNHEALTHY BELIEF.

It is an unhealthy belief that causes the phobia.

And an unhealthy belief has its own demands. It might be that the phobia-suffering individual says: *"I hope I'm not going to see a spider"* and/or *"I mustn't even start to think about spiders."*

Unhealthy beliefs are unrealistic, they are irrational, they are rigid and they are unhelpful.

Unhealthy beliefs can lead to:

Frustration – *"I can't stand it"*

Catastrophising – *"this is the worst thing that could happen, I'd rather shoot myself than see a spider"*

Self-damnation or the condemnation of others: *"I'm pathetic for being scared of spiders"* or

"You're useless, why haven't you made sure there aren't any spiders in the house?"

It takes only one of these reactions to cause unhealthy negative emotions.

So the next step is to decide how we are going to treat this.

The answer is that we need to swap our unhealthy beliefs for healthy beliefs.

If I take myself as an example: I have a healthy belief about spiders. I am not a big fan of spiders but I don't go around the house checking to see if any are lurking and if I do happen to notice one it is not going to scare me – I have a high frustration tolerance (in other words, I can cope); I don't catastrophise: I know the world is not going to stop turning if I see a spider and, finally, I am fallible – I might feel uncomfortable picking up an exceptionally large, hairy spider and letting it crawl up my arm but that is not going to make me feel any worse about myself when I politely decline to pick it up.

Individuals with healthy beliefs about spiders do not actively go around searching for them.

They simply hold a PREFERENCE. *"I'd rather not see one of them, thank you very much."*

It is easy to become confused about negative emotions. We are told that negative emotions are bad – "try to be positive" is an example of well-intended advice.

But quite often we need negative emotions – they help protect us from real dangers. We need to retain **rational concern**.

Take for a moment someone who has a fear of traffic. I would not hypnotise them and then tell them that traffic is completely safe. They need to have rational concern. If they step in front of a moving bus it will most likely kill them. But cross the road where it is safe to do so and they need not be anxious about traffic.

Anxiety is an UNHEALTHY negative emotion.

By holding a HEALTHY preference – eg I'd rather not see a spider, or I'd rather not be hit by the 56 bus – we have changed what was an UNHEALTHY negative emotion into a HEALTHY negative emotion.

The HEALTHY preference enables the individual to view a threat realistically.

If a person is concerned about an event as opposed to being anxious, it does not mean that they are indifferent about that event.

Are you still wondering where smoking fits into all this?

The answer is: beliefs. Or you might call it perception.

CHAPTER EIGHTEEN
Embracing change

We have established already that the perception that giving up cigarettes is going to be difficult is not a result of chemical addiction but a FEAR of being unable to cope; the FEAR of anxiety.

And anxiety is an UNHEALTHY negative emotion.

We need to change that UNHEALTHY negative emotion.

As a practitioner who uses cognitive behavioural therapy, (CBT) I know that people can change.

I will look at the distinction between other emotions to help further demonstrate my point.

Anger - Annoyance

Anger is an unhealthy negative emotion.
Annoyance is a healthy negative emotion.

Most of us will have been in a supermarket at some time and witnessed a toddler throwing a tantrum because the parent won't open some packet of sweets or is perhaps refusing to buy the child a new toy. Your thoughts might be that you're just glad you're not in charge of that youngster and you might, at the same time, feel a little bit of sympathy for the parent. Yet, irritating though the child's behaviour might be, you tolerate the child's behaviour because you know what children are like. You also know children will grow up – in other words they will grow out of throwing tantrums. They will change.

This might seem fairly obvious – most people in society mature and take on a healthy belief. They PREFER to get their own way but they do not always demand it or condemn another person if they fail to get what they want. But perhaps they adhere to this in some circumstances but not in others. There are some instances when the toddler re-emerges.

Take an angry motorist, as an example – perhaps he is the purple-faced driver stuck behind you at traffic lights who is yelling and blasting his horn. Is he an innately angry person or can he change? Of course, he can change. His anger makes him a danger to himself and other road users. He needs to accept that he would PREFER that the road was clear but he cannot demand it nor blame other drivers.

When angry, people will react in different ways, some might even physically assault another person. Others do not show these action tendencies. But they might still harbour the emotion of that physically violent person.

Their emotions are known as META-emotions (an emotion about an emotion).

And people may tranquilise their feelings with unhealthy habits – heavy drinking or smoking, for example.

But by choosing to replace an unhealthy negative emotion with a healthy negative emotion a person seizes personal control.

I am not suggesting that you be happy about the events that trigger negative emotions, I am telling you to try to hold a PREFERENCE.

For example, I am not happy about being stuck in this traffic but I prefer being here rather than in hospital with a stroke induced by a meta-emotion or having sped off the wrong way down a one-way street and crashed.

Take another example. You would prefer your boss not to be so critical at work. But you can tolerate it. It is not the end of the world. Your boss is fallible just as you are, just as is every human being. There is no need for you to express anger or to harbour anger.

It is he (or she) who is the one with the problem.

But how do we deal with the injustice of a boss behaving nastily?

I teach people to have **rational confidence** so that they feel able to be assertive when appropriate.

They can request change but not demand it. They are usually amazed by the positive effect that rational confidence has on all aspects of their lives.

I have had many such clients who have come back to me to tell me that since embracing this ethos they have earned a promotion or achieved the pay rise that they knew they deserved.

As I keep insisting: I know people can change.

What is important is that people understand the value of being tolerant.

They must recognise that people are fallible – they must not always see malice in a person's actions.

Rationality has to be applied.

Let us take a look at how all this this relates to smoking.

The fear of giving up smoking is conditioned anxiety.
(See appendix: anxiety and excitement)
We need to change that emotion – to hold a preference.

We need to acknowledge our perceptions.

The smoker needs to acknowledge that it is fear he or she fears and instead to hold a preference – to swap fear for concern – to swap an unhealthy emotion for a healthy emotion. Constructive concern for one's well-being is preferred over fear of anxiety.

Among intriguing examples that support my tenet linking smoking with anxiety are those clients who happened to have been smokers who came to me, not to stop smoking but seeking help for anxiety and later contacted me to say that following treatment their newly-gained insight into their behaviour had also led them to give up cigarettes.

One woman who got in touch said she no longer suffered panic attacks, adding: *"I also suddenly realised I didn't have to smoke anymore. It just seemed ridiculous to light up a cigarette. So I've stopped and it doesn't bother me at all."*

In a personal, face-to-face consultation at my clinic it is easier for the client to grasp my reasoning because I am able to sense whether a point has been understood or missed and I can endeavour to give a different example to clear up any incomprehension or miscomprehension.

Likewise the client is free to ask as many questions as he or she likes.

In Section Three of this book I have included a list of Frequently Asked Questions, which, although not exhaustive, I hope will go some way to resolving any outstanding issues readers might have.

Hopefully, you will recognise how obvious it is why you have continued to smoke in spite of your recognition of the harm it is doing you.

Understanding your disorder is the key to stopping.

And you know that having made the decision to quit, achievement is going to be easy.
You have taken emotional responsibility.

CHAPTER NINETEEN
Trance states

Once clients indicate that they understand the nature of their disorder it is time to move to the next stage.

At the clinic, this usually involves integrating healthy beliefs into the unconscious through hypnosis. We will be nailing down these truths in your mind.

I first of all check that the client wants to continue to this next level.

The consultation has provided an intellectual insight – hypnosis provides an emotional insight.

If we are in agreement about proceeding with hypnosis, the session can begin immediately, or if the client prefers, he or she can come back at a later date.

I also instruct clients at my clinic how to practise self-hypnosis, if they wish, as a means for them to reaffirm what they have learnt. (In Section Two, you will find a guide to self-hypnosis. Please practise these techniques in order to become a non-smoker.)

Clients at the clinic wanting to benefit from hypnosis are put into a trance.

For anyone who might still harbour misgivings about hypnosis, let me reiterate that there is no cause for alarm and please be assured that treatment is conducted under strict ethical conditions and that clients remain in full control throughout the process. They cannot be compelled to do anything they do not wish.

For those disinclined to believe this claim, perhaps because of what is suggested on television and in fiction, I offer a fuller explanation in the appendix. *(See appendix: Stage hypnosis).*

As I point out on my website, everybody has experienced different levels of trance at some stage in their life, whether or not they are aware of the fact.

For example, waking hypnosis can occur naturally when someone's attention is focused on a specific matter – while they have been daydreaming for instance.

Other states of hypnosis include a state when an individual is falling asleep (the hypnogogic state) or when waking up (the hypnopompic state).

These are light trances.

There are three depths of trance, though, and the properly trained therapist can guide a patient into as deep a state as the client will allow.

Remember our unconscious minds are always concerned and view any danger realistically. I am able only to give clients positive beneficial suggestions.

It is while in a state of hypnosis, that the patient's resolve and understanding are reinforced in his or her unconscious, providing a continuing source of inner-strength.

No-one knows exactly how much of the brain is employed in conscious thought but it is estimated it may be below even ten per cent.

That means that 90 per cent or more of the brain's capacity is given over to unconscious matters, what is more commonly known as the subconscious.

Stored in the unconscious are a person's knowledge, learnt skills, attitudes, habits and beliefs as well as control of such automatic functions as breathing and heart rate.

For some, the hardest concept when considering clinical hypnotherapy treatment is to comprehend that it is possible for them to be put into a hypnotic state.

I consider this to be the easiest part of treatment.

It is fair to say that there are some practitioners who find putting patients into a trance a challenge and inevitably they will find some clients are more resistant than others.

When I demonstrate techniques to students on behalf of the London School of Clinical Hypnosis, I can sense the concern of some in their ability to induce a state of trance in their subjects. But it is a skill and it has to be learnt. Once mastered, though, it is possible to put a person in a hypnotic state almost instantaneously and there are a number of techniques that can be employed depending on a client's character.

For the purposes of treatment, I regard it as most effective to ease a willing client into a hypnotic state slowly and gently, yet keeping them focused.

The smoker seeking help is at ease and comfortable.

Once he or she is at a deep enough level of receptive relaxation I allow the patient to accept all the reasoning as to why living without cigarettes is going to be easy.

There is no need for the soon-to-be non-smoker to be worried about physical addiction. Just as nicotine enters the system almost immediately through the inhalation of tobacco smoke, so the poison leaves the body's nervous system quickly.

That physical addiction is very short-lived — very short-lived, indeed.

Yet it is those first few hours of physical withdrawal that some smokers who want to give up fear the most.

But they have no reason to feel concerned.

The confidence, self-belief, well-being and sense of joy following a session of hypnosis will carry the now non-smoker through that initial stage with ease.

Cravings will be negated.

When individuals come out of the hypnotised state, they feel more relaxed and calmer than they have felt in years.

They have been in my room for about two-and-a-half hours without having had a cigarette.

There are some smokers who try to give up by themselves and employ non-hypnotic techniques but whose joy at giving up cigarettes is enough to carry them over that physical addiction barrier with ease and, happily, some never go back to smoking.

For some others, though, once their initial enthusiasm fades, their resolve weakens as well and they find themselves back on cigarettes all too quickly or in some cases after days of torment, finally succumbing when the pressure becomes just too much to bear. (And some become self-loathing for failing).

What is happening in such cases is that people mistake their thoughts about smoking as being their physical addiction reasserting itself.

It is not.

They have gone through that barrier already.

As I have already explained, it is the mind playing tricks.

The individual trying to quit without guidance might continue to suffer as time passes and might no longer feel like a non-smoker but instead like a smoker still struggling to give up.

The thought of smoking simply refuses to leave them and their confidence in being able to resist erodes.

The thought of smoking haunts them almost constantly and seems to intensify as the hours/days go by rather than abate.

Their thoughts have become obsessive.

The danger is that they then relapse and are soon back smoking as many cigarettes as they had been before they began trying to stop. They are compulsive.

For those who have undertaken clinical hypnosis treatment, such minefields are avoided.

Reasoning has been anchored in the unconscious.

The client comprehends how irrational it is that he or she would ever want to smoke.

The FEAR of not smoking – which has scuppered those previous attempts to give up – now no longer exists.

They do not have to worry about intrusive thoughts that have until now been a huge source of anxiety – being anxious about being anxious.

CHAPTER TWENTY
Intrusive thoughts

We have now returned to the point we were at the start of this book when I first mentioned intrusive thoughts, alluding to the fact that to the smoker who wants to quit but has no understanding of his or her condition, intrusive thoughts are their greatest fear.

It is the intrusive thought that will constantly threaten to undermine their resolve – that is, their perception.

But intrusive thoughts need pose no threat.
They are easily neutralised.

I had a client who came to see me once, not about smoking but about a recurring image that was troubling her deeply.

She said: *"Daniel, I watched a horror movie a few months ago and since then I've not been able to get this image out of my head. It's horrible. But it just won't go away. I've got to the point where I'm beginning to think that I'm evil; I don't think it can be right having these kinds of thoughts, can it?"*

I told her she wasn't evil. But she was unable to comprehend that a good person would think about what she had seen in the film.

To treat her, I pointed out that I myself am neither a saint nor a demon. But I am allowed to think about the very same scene she was referring to – the one that troubled her so much. I PREFER not to have the image in my mind but I am not going to punish myself if that's what happens. It would feel uncomfortable and I PREFER not to feel uncomfortable – but I do not demand it. I accept that I am allowed these thoughts. In fact, if I think of the film writers who first constructed this image or the director of the movie, I very much doubt that they punish themselves. They embraced the thought initially and used it for artistic effect. By including it in the film, they acknowledged that it invoked emotion, that it would make viewers feel anxious or excited. *(See appendix: Anxiety and excitement)*.

It is for this reason that people watch horror movies, which take advantage of innate fears, notably loud, unexpected noises, depth perception (somebody coming onto screen very quickly) and scowling/snarling faces.

For my client, though, the image had been haunting her. It was a recurring intrusive thought.

So, let me introduce a rather different intrusive thought… it is a cliché… the pink elephant.

It is not scary or exciting but if I was to tell someone that they were not allowed to think of a pink elephant and added the suggestion that something bad would happen if they happened to do so, they are going to find it very difficult for the image not to appear. And the likelihood is that the more they try not to think about the pink elephant the more it comes into their mind's eye.

They would probably start to panic if they truly held the belief that thinking about the pink elephant could really cause them harm. They might even suffer a panic attack.

But we all know it is permissible to think about pink elephants without consequence. It is not going to make us anxious if we do so and this means the thought will soon flow away and intrude less and less frequently.

It should now be recognised that every intrusive thought that a person has is no more than the equivalent of the pink elephant.

People sometimes ask me: *"Doesn't it upset you having to work with so many people's difficulties? Don't you become upset?"*

My answer is: I am saddened to see people suffer but I am allowed to think about what they have told me and embrace the thoughts so that I am able to help them.

There will even be situations in my own life when I will remember what a client has told me but I do not worry that I am going to start suffering from the same condition.

90

I am not going to be intimidated by my imagination.

I know there are things that I do not like that make me feel uncomfortable but I am allowed to think these things and laugh at the trick of the mind. I am allowed to become a little over excited – even the physical symptoms cannot really cause me harm. (As discussed in the Appendix *Anxiety and excitement,* these two emotions share identical physical symptoms.) In fact, the more I allow the thought in, the more I am able to rationalise it for what it is; just a fictitious part of my imagination.

So, how has this got anything to do with smoking?

Well, what a smoker thinks when trying to quit often follows a similar pattern. They wake up and they have breakfast. Now, let's suppose their habit was usually to have a cigarette after breakfast. They will begin to think: *"I'd be having a cigarette right now if I hadn't given up. I've got to stop thinking about them. I can't. I must not think about cigarettes."*

And there, sitting in his or her mind is the image of a cigarette. They might even be able to believe they can smell it.

They might start to shake and think: *"I'm suffering nicotine withdrawal. I'm an addict. I don't think I can stand this."*

What in fact is happening is that they are scaring themselves about the thought of – not a pink elephant – but a cigarette. They are becoming over-excited by the thought. They believe that the physical symptoms – racing heart, sweating, tension – are symptoms of physical withdrawal. But they are not. It is stimulation, over-excitement, triggered by intrusive thoughts.

Later in the day, when their mind is occupied by some task, they will forget about smoking. When not distracted, the intrusive thought returns and the fear or over-excitement is back. Once the person understands how to deal with the intrusive thoughts and adrenalin which is released in the body by excitement, the problem disappears.

Non-smokers, of course, are able to think of cigarettes whenever they want. They do not scare themselves about the thought.

At my clinic, I provide the client – through hypnotherapy – with the conviction that they are a non-smoker and with that comes confidence.

As a non-smoker you are allowed to think about smoking whenever you want, without over-excitement. I'm getting you to embrace the thought of cigarettes.

No longer will you confuse fear or over-excitement with nicotine withdrawal. By embracing the thought, rather than trying to banish it, you are able to rationalise what smoking is and what it does to you. Your unconscious will rationalise that smoking is entirely negative. You will begin to despise smoking. I want you to hate smoking and the tobacco industry because you finally see the truth clearly and without fear.

You now have the freedom to make the correct decision. The compulsion to smoke has been eradicated.

One additional point to make is that I am aware that some ex-smokers when they are asleep dream that they are back smoking.

But, again, that is not something to fear.

If that happens to you, simply embrace the joy when you wake up that you are no longer a smoker.

Cigarettes no longer have any hold on you.

The power of hypnosis welds the truth of this statement into your mind – what I have referred to already as an integration into the unconscious.

It might be reassuring to know that the therapist also anticipates those situations when the temptation to relapse might arise.

Smokers who come to see me before treatment might well have a good idea when such instances are most likely to occur and you probably do too – they will be at times when anxiety levels are raised.

For the client who has been treated through hypnosis, the resolve and reason lodged in the unconscious will be activated at the first hint of raised anxiety.

One occasion when a relapse might be a threat is when someone has been drinking to excess. The problem with alcohol, to use non-professional terminology, is that it can temporarily unwire the unconscious, when taken in too large a quantity, in other words when the client is drunk.

I am not, by the way, addressing problems associated with alcoholism, which is another issue. (For the record, I also treat this condition, though there are stronger physiological issues associated with alcohol than with smoking).

For anyone who enjoys a drink in moderation, it is possible to lay safeguards in the unconscious to discourage a smoking relapse. If drinking is a problem and you lapsed before, a simple solution is to take emotional responsibility and not get hopelessly drunk. Take responsibility.

I recall working with a client a little while ago. He had been to see me three years earlier wanting to stop smoking. Treatment had been successful and for three years he had not smoked or been troubled by it. And then one Sunday morning he phoned me in a panic.

"I need your help. I can't believe what's happened. I've started smoking again."

I made an appointment for him the same day. The client said he had been at a wedding the previous day and had had too much to drink and he had smoked a cigar. When he arrived at my clinic he was obviously very anxious.

"I can't believe I've started smoking again after all these years," he kept repeating. *"I need you to repeat the magic trick again."*

Well, much as I might like the idea of being a wizard, hypnotherapy is not a magic trick.

This gentleman had simply made a mistake. He was judging himself as being a failure because of a single slip-up, because of one error.

His feeling of guilt had triggered a meta-emotion of anxiety.

He was afraid he was now a smoker again and was again confusing anxiety with nicotine withdrawal.

We reframed the mistake: I would have preferred not to have become so drunk that I smoked a cigar. But I did and while that is regrettable I still deserve to be a non-smoker because I am still concerned about my well-being.

We always have a choice.

If I was to have approached this man at the wedding when he was about to light the cigar and offered him a huge, life-changing sum of money not to smoke that cigar and he believed that my offer was a sincere one, then he would almost certainly have taken the money and left the cigar.

If I was then to have seen him the following day and he had been diagnosed with a terminal illness that was smoking-related but was told that if he handed back the money I had given him the previous day he would be cured, then he would almost certainly surrender his fortune just as he did the cigar.

The logic is that his health is worth more than a smoke.

He knows that.

He has a choice.

He has taken emotional responsibility.

And in life we all have to take emotional responsibility.

It is the hypnotherapist's job to help the smoker to recognise this simple fact of life.

CHAPTER TWENTY-ONE
Quick summary

I thought it would be helpful to summarise the steps detailed in this book on how to become a non-smoker and stay a non-smoker. Hopefully, you will now better understand the essential elements of treatment.

1. You recognise that you need and want to stop smoking for your own sake and for the sake of all those who love you. Grasp responsibility (self-efficacy).
2. You might find it helpful to list all the negative aspects of smoking and also all the positive aspects of not being a smoker. This will help emphasise the logic of your decision to quit.
3. You now understand your condition. Smoking is primarily a psychological condition.
4. You understand "The Power of Now". What you might have once believed was physical dependency can be broken instantly. Once you have determined that you are a non-smoker you become one with immediate effect. Remember there is no qualifying period. Once you stop, you are a non-smoker.

5. You now have no fear of a future without cigarettes. You accept that what you once thought of as physical dependency was a psychological issue that you have addressed. Your fear that created anxiety has gone. You realise that what you once thought of as physical withdrawal symptoms were merely the anxiety you now no longer experience.

6. You are empowered. You have taken emotional responsibility. You realise fear is a conditioned response – an unhealthy negative emotion.

7. You no longer fear intrusive thoughts.

8. You might wish to seek the help of a clinical hypnotherapist able to integrate your new-found comprehension into your unconscious through trance or you might wish to practise self-hypnosis *(See Section Two)*. But for many of you, simply grasping the logic and principles detailed in Section One will be enough to enable you to accept that it is indeed a doddle to stop smoking.

9. You can embrace the joy of no longer being a smoker.

10. You can let others know how easy it is to stop.

Section Two
Self-hypnosis

CHAPTER TWENTY-TWO
Your guide to self-hypnosis

While treatment by a trained hypnotherapist is likely to be more efficacious than self-hypnosis, the latter can nevertheless be very useful, not only for relaxation purposes but also as a means of achieving a specific goal, for example smoking cessation. If you are committed to being a non-smoker and are able to adhere to these instructions that follow, then YOU WILL BECOME A NON-SMOKER.

Please note that the sections entitled Anchor, Parts Therapy, Aversion, Authoritarian and Motivational self-hypnosis are alternative techniques and should be used in separate sessions of self-hypnosis.

Planning
Plan ahead – ensure you have a suitable room where you are not going to be disturbed; turn off your mobile phone etc. Try to have the room at a temperature that feels agreeable and wear comfortable clothing.

You may wish to lie down, though you don't want to fall asleep, so a comfy chair might be better.

Have in your mind what you want to achieve – in this instance it is to stop smoking. I would expect that by now you have considered the main points contained in Section One of the book and understand that you have the power of self-determination – you are ready to take responsibility.

It might help to rehearse the suggestions you are going to make during your period of self-hypnosis.

If you think it will help you, then write these down or use suggestions contained in the text that follows.

Now close your eyes and relax.

Inducing trance

If thoughts enter your mind at this stage don't fight them... just take your time and relax – concentrate on your breathing. Breathe in slowly through your nose, for about six seconds and then hold your breath for four seconds and then exhale slowly for about ten seconds but not completely and then hold your breath again for four seconds. Now inhale again slowly and hold your breath – exhale slowly and hold your breath. Continue this pattern and you will begin to feel relaxed. (We all have different lung capacities so breathing out for nearly twice as long as you breathe-in is a good guideline.) You might find it helpful to imagine positive colours in the air when you inhale. Your eyelids may feel heavy but this is a pleasant feeling – slowly the tension in your body is ebbing away. Be aware of your body as if it is floating and then focus on your toes and let them relax. You may feel a pleasant tingling sensation in your toes. You can sense the tension leaving and it is a nice feeling – now move your mind slowly up your body freeing each section of remaining stress. Move your mind from your toes to the rest of your feet, and then to your ankles, then to your shins, your knees, thighs and so on, all the time abandoning stress as you go. You are breathing out all that stress. Relax your neck. Your body seems to become lighter, as in turn you allow each section of tension to drift away. You might like to imagine a warm stream is flowing over your body, washing away all anxiety. Your whole body is relaxed. Visualise this in your own mind. Continue to breathe slowly and let your mind visualise what it wishes, embracing the images gently, imagining the touch and the smell. Things that have troubled you are floating away and you realise how trivial such matters really are.

All the time, try not to demand that you feel more relaxed than you do – simply enjoy the process and PREFER to feel relaxed. Your unconscious will allow you to go as deep as you need to. Take all the time you need in order to practise the technique. Although you will be relaxed, it is important also to be focused.

Practise your ratio breathing technique regularly for a few minutes at a time. Soon you will become adept at entering into a relaxed/focused trance state.

At this stage you may begin to feel your mind drifting and if so bring back focus and concentrate on yourself. You're beginning to become conscious of being unconscious.

Let the feeling of relaxation progress into your stomach. Be in the present, fully focused on the relaxed feelings. You are in the Now. Those wonderful pleasant feelings can then flow into your back, chest and body muscles. Let the body sink deeper and more comfortably into the chair.

Let your shoulders loosen, releasing all tension, as if you've just untied a shoe lace by gently pulling the loose end.

Finally, relax your arms and let your hands and fingers relax in the same way you allowed your toes to relax. You may feel a slight numbness in your fingers and throughout your body. This is perfectly fine – you are entering into a natural and comfortable meditative hypnotic trance.

Deepening a trance

This technique can be used by itself as an induction or can be used to deepen a trance.

Counting down from ten to one is a common way to induce/deepen trance. Count down every other time you breathe out. You could begin to use imagery at this point, for example you might imagine yourself walking down a safe, well-lit path with a handrail. With each step you take down the path, count down as you breathe out and feel more relaxed. Once at the bottom of the path, step into your favourite place of relaxation. This can be any place you wish. Always remember that you can instantly return to this favourite place of yours anytime you wish to while in trance.

When in this state there are a range of techniques that can then be employed, all of the following being effective:

TECHNIQUES TO CHOOSE FROM
Any one of these techniques can be used while in trance, once the methodology for entering and deepening a trance state has been mastered.

Each technique will have to be memorised so that you know exactly what you are doing at each step once you are in trance.

Technique One
ANCHORS

Step 1
Go back to a time and place when you had a feeling of calmness and relaxation. Make the image as real as you can. See what you saw then, feel what you felt then, smell what you smelt then. Use all of your senses as if you were there right now. Allow these relaxing feelings to grow stronger and stronger. When you experience these feelings, place the tip of your thumb against the tip of your middle or index finger.

Step 2
Bring all those feelings forward with you. Imagine yourself now in a situation where you would be likely to have a cigarette. Now once again place the tip of your finger against your thumb and allow all of those wonderful relaxing feelings to return to your body, remembering the feelings that the past relaxing situation gave you. Practise this until you really feel those wonderful feelings.

Step 3

Repeat this three more times, going back to different situations when you had feelings of calmness and relaxation. (This is to ensure that the anchor, ie placing the tip of thumb and finger together, is conditioned so that you associate this gesture with calmness and relaxation.)

Step 4

Once this is complete, drift back in time to a situation where you had feelings of confidence, strength and accomplishment. Again, make the image as real as you can. See what you saw then, feel what you felt then, smell what you smelt then. Use all of your senses as if you are there. Allow these feelings to grow stronger and stronger. When you feel this strength, clench your fist tightly. Allow those wonderful strong feelings to course through your whole body.

Step 5

Bring all those feelings forward with you. Imagine yourself now in a situation where you would normally have a cigarette. Now clench your fist tightly and allow all of those wonderful confident feelings to return to your body, remembering the confident feelings of strength that the past event gave you. Practise this until you really feel those wonderful feelings.

Step 6

Once again repeat this three more times going back to different situations when you had feelings of confidence, control and accomplishment.

Step 7

Before waking from trance, it is useful to strengthen your ego and confidence and for you to look to the future to see yourself as the confident and healthy non-smoker that you now are. In your unconscious, you can project yourself forward a week, a month or years ahead, still healthy and full of confidence. Make these images as clear as you can, perhaps seeing children or grandchildren growing up and you enjoying a full and rewarding life.

● **Waking from trance** – when you decide it is time to emerge from trance, count in your mind from one to ten and at each ascending number you will become more alert; by the count of eight you open your eyes, raise your head and smile; every healthy part of you, now a non-smoker will by the count of ten be back in the room and every normal, healthy sensation will return to your body and limbs. You will feel refreshed and motivated.

Technique Two
PARTS THERAPY

Step 1

Once you have achieved a relaxing depth of trance, allow yourself to imagine "the Part of yourself that has been responsible for your unhealthy smoking habit". By the Part, I mean what you consider to be your reason or excuse for smoking – for example, you might consider smoking has provided you with the opportunity to take a break from work. You need to see the Part that is responsible for you smoking as an image in your mind's eye – just relax and your unconscious will provide you with an image, perhaps a shape or a colour (your own unconscious will decide this). You may want to visualise this Part drifting out of your body. The Part can appear to be any size, shape, or colour. Make sure you fully visualise this Part.

Step 2

Once you can visualise this Part allow yourself to communicate with it. Thank it for coming forward and for being willing to communicate with you and ask it its name.

Thank the Part for the perceived help it has been offering. Do this wholeheartedly. It may seem bizarre to thank the Part, but it is essential. The Part has been trying to help you; it is not your enemy. It was confused in thinking that smoking might help you cope with difficult, external events and stresses. Because it has been trying to help you, I would like you to forgive it. Again, do this wholeheartedly.

Step 3

Once you have forgiven the Part, communicate with it and come to an agreement with it that it will transform into something that is going to assist you in being a healthy individual by giving up smoking. (It is your unconscious that will determine what that something will be – ie how it will be represented in your mind's eye.)

Step 4

Once this is agreed, you can begin the transformation. Visualise the Part in the process of transforming. Allow the size, shape and colour of this Part to emerge. Feel the power and confidence that occurs within you as this transformation takes place.

Step 5

Once you have allowed the Part responsible for your old outgrown smoking habit to be fully transformed, thank it again.

Step 6

Before waking from trance, it is useful to strengthen your ego and confidence and for you to look to the future to see yourself as the confident and healthy non-smoker that you now are. In your unconscious, you can project yourself forward a week, a month or years ahead, still healthy and full of confidence. Make these images as clear as you can, perhaps seeing children or grandchildren growing up and you enjoying a full and rewarding life.

• **Waking from trance** – when you decide it is time to emerge from trance, count in your mind from one to ten and at each ascending number you will become more alert; by the count of eight you open your eyes, raise your head and smile; every healthy part of you, now a non-smoker, will by the count of ten be back in the room and every normal, healthy sensation will return to your body and limbs. You will feel refreshed and motivated.

Technique Three
AVERSION THERAPY

This technique is particularly effective if an individual has a strong aversion to something – so strong in fact that the thought of it makes them feel sick – perhaps rotting food in the fridge or dog muck on your shoes. If there is anything you are averse to, then use it. It works wonders.

In trance, you will focus on the aversion forming an association with smoking so that any time you think of a cigarette you will associate it with your aversion. Make the image as clear in your mind's eye as is possible until the thought turns your stomach. Imagine the object of your disgust being placed in a cigarette packet and that very same packet being sold to you and when opening it...

As already stated in the techniques above, before waking from trance, it is useful to strengthen your ego and confidence and for you to look to the future to see yourself as the confident and healthy non-smoker that you now are. In your unconscious, project yourself forward a week, a month or years ahead, still healthy and full of confidence. Make these images as clear as you can, perhaps seeing children or grandchildren growing up and you enjoying a full and rewarding life.

● **Waking from trance** – when you decide it is time to emerge from trance, count in your mind from one to ten and at each ascending number you will become more alert; by the count of eight you open your eyes, raise your head and smile; every healthy part of you, now a non-smoker, will by the count of ten be back in the room and every normal, healthy sensation will return to your body and limbs. You will feel refreshed and motivated.

Technique Four
AUTHORITARIAN & MOTIVATIONAL THERAPY

A slightly different approach to inducing trance is used in this technique as it is a no nonsense, no excuse approach to stopping smoking. This approach will help you be motivated and empower you.

Before beginning, write down what you are going to tell yourself and prepare to tell it firmly. The technique is a metaphorical slap across the face – a no-nonsense wake-up call. Write down all the excuses you have ever made for being a smoker and/or for not having given up. Look at these excuses, rip them up. They are rubbish.

Now write down and think about all the negative connotations associated with smoking. Here are a few suggestions to work with. You might care to first of all wander around your town and spot smokers outside offices – watch how they behave.

People think smokers are lazy, needing an excuse for a break;

People think smokers have no will power;

People think smokers smell bad;

People think smokers can't cope;

People think smokers are selfish;

People think smokers are stupid (spending that amount on cigarettes and ruining their health);

People think smokers are unhealthy;

People think smokers are unattractive.

If you're a parent think about what your children will think of you as a smoker. If you're a grandparent think of denying yourself the opportunity of seeing those children grow up.

Consider the health consequences of smoking:

Cancer;

Heart disease;

Early ageing – wrinkled skin;

High blood pressure;

Anxiety.

The list could go on.

I want you to begin to hate smoking for what it has turned you into and what it is doing to you. And then think of all those wealthy tobacco bosses growing richer and smirking at you as your health declines. You are seeing smoking for what it is. Use your own words to tell yourself what you think. Use bad language if you want. You will now need to memorise everything you have written down.

When you are ready to induce trance, sit down and make sure that you are sitting straight with your head held up high. Begin by simply closing your eyes. Count yourself down from ten to one, however unlike the relaxation meditative trances, this will be a focused trance. You expand a focused concentration on becoming smoke free.

Once in trance the suggestions you give to yourself will be very much your own words ie what you have written down and memorised. Now you begin to tell yourself:

"No longer am I going to come up with pathetic EXCUSES;

"No longer am I going to smell bad;

"No longer am I going to let myself be regarded as a pitiful, hopeless loser;

"I am going to be a confident, attractive, healthy person. (Emphasise the "I" by calling yourself by name)

"I am commanding my unconscious that I am smoke free. I am supercharging my unconscious and I will be a successful, healthy smoke-free person.

"I am drilling into my mind that no longer will I allow cigarettes and the tobacco bosses to manipulate me;

"I am drilling it into my mind that I am taking full responsibility.

"No longer will I waste my money on cigarettes, ruin my lungs on cigarettes. No more.

"I can see clearly… I see myself as a healthy responsible person."

Speak these words aloud if you want. Shout them if you want. Tell the tobacco bosses what you think of them.

Once you've given yourself these direct instructions, look into the future.

Feel how great it is to be a non-smoker. Focus on that feeling and the image in your mind. Have attitude. Lift your head up high, take a deep breath. Imagine looking around and seeing those people who are important to you congratulating you. See how healthy you are. Use all your senses, notice how you smell, see how your skin feels rejuvenated.

Play this movie in your mind over, again and again. Use a record you like that you deem as motivational. Start to hum it as you go through the movie in your mind. Tell your unconscious that you are going to supercharge it up and that it is going to do exactly AS YOU TELL IT. You tell it that excuses are no longer acceptable. You tell it that you are a successful non-smoker. Turn up the volume of your instructions, and tell your unconscious that you will enhance these instructions three fold with each clap. Clap your hands as you hum your motivational record.

As you count up from one to ten you lift up your head high and smile, feeling more confident with each number. At the count of eight, stand up dancing on your tip toes. At the count of ten, walk away as a non-smoker.

Section Three
CONCLUSION

I am confident that smokers who grasp the explanations and follow the instructions contained in this book will have no difficulty in becoming non-smokers. It is my hope that, in addition, the book provides readers with a broader insight into hypnotherapy that reveals just how useful the practice can be in the treatment of a wide range of conditions.

I always welcome the comments and observations of my clients and, likewise, I am happy to receive feedback from readers of this book by email via my website: www.leeds-hypnotherapy-clinic.co.uk.

I wish you all a happy, smoke-free future.

Daniel L McDermid

APPENDIX

PANIC *(Page 9)*

Heightened anxiety can lead to panic. In extreme cases people may think that they are dying. They can be very frightened. The sufferer feels dizzy and the panic begins to take a grip; they begin to breathe heavily; they introduce too much CO_2 into their brains which causes them to become more light-headed and they introduce excess oxygen into the blood stream, accelerating the heart rate.

"Why is my heart racing, why am I getting dizzy? I'm dying," they might tell themselves.

They are not dying, they are panicking.

I recall that once when giving blood I experienced sudden dizziness. I felt uncomfortable but because I understood what was happening I did not panic. I knew that I preferred not to pass out but knew that even if I did, I would be safe if I sat down. By not panicking I did not exacerbate my condition through heavy breathing. By not panicking about panic, the body soon returned to its normal state.

In the same way the smoker wishing to quit avoids anxiety by not being fearful of fear.

It is useful to recognise that excitement and fear create the same symptoms. It is our interpretation of these symptoms caused by

119

adrenaline that determines whether we are fearful or exhilarated.

Obsessive Compulsive Disorders *(Page 13)*
Obsessive compulsive disorder (OCD) can be defined as a subclass of anxiety disorders. Its characteristics are recurring ideas, thoughts and feelings and repetitive, often ritualised, behaviour. The urge to indulge the obsession creates anxiety that is then relieved by performing the ritual.

"The term is not properly used for behaviours like excessive drinking, gambling, eating etc. on the grounds that the 'compulsive gambler,' for example, actually derives considerable pleasure from gambling (it's the losing that hurts): one burdened with a true obsessive compulsive disorder derives no pleasure from it other than the release of tension." (*Arthur S Reber, Dictionary of Psychology, Penguin*)

This definition, it might be concluded, excludes smoking from being categorised as an OCD because of the pleasure element.

My argument for adopting similar techniques to treat smokers to those I would use to treat an OCD is that the so-called pleasure derived from smoking is illusory. This illusory pleasure is simply the relief of anxiety which has itself been caused by the practice of smoking.

Placebo effect *(Page 30)*

The placebo effect is a recognised phenomenon. It involves treatment of a condition based on the trust of the patient in the treatment rather than any actual medical intervention. Its effectiveness indicates the brain's powerful role in physical health.

Self-efficacy *(Page 33)*

According to psychologist Albert Bandura, self-efficacy is *"the belief in one's capabilities to organize and execute the courses of action required to manage prospective situations"*.

He wrote that people have goals and things they would like to change about themselves or their situations – either obstacles to be avoided or challenges to overcome.

In the following quotations from conclusions by Professor Bandura, NRT stands for Nicotine Replacement Therapy, eg the use of e-cigarettes etc.

"Our confidence in quitting smoking has been constantly shaken for decades by the saturation of NRT advertising, which insists that quitting smoking is a painful, life wreaking upheaval…"

"The failure of most of the smoking cessation programs, including NRT treatments, most likely seems to be due to negligence of including self-efficacy as an imperative factor to motivating smokers to quit."

I would describe self-efficacy as confidence and self-acceptance. It is a matter of accepting one's "fallibilities".

An example is the client who comes to my clinic and asks: "Can you cure me of blushing?"

My answer is: "No. But I can help you overcome your phobia of blushing."

Once the client is no longer anxious about blushing, the problem goes away. He or she has gained confidence.

But confidence itself is much misunderstood… the most confident person is one who will let go of his or her pride. Yet pride is part of the human condition. We can only moderate it. No-one wants to be seen as a vulnerable person – yet we are all fallible. The most we can do is be conscious of our unconscious – mindful of our thoughts, feelings and emotions.

British Society of Clinical Hypnosis *(Page 36)*
   125, Queensgate Bridlington, East Yorkshire YO16 7JQ
   Tel: 01262 403 103
   Fax: 01262 403 103
   Website: www.bsch.org.uk

Stage hypnosis *(Pages 38 & 82)*

I always assure clients of the ethical nature of my treatment and that the client in trance always remains in control and cannot be compelled to do anything he or she does not wish.

I have stated in this book that manipulation by stage hypnotists can give the impression that the subject is acting out of character but that this is not the case, or at least it is not a result of hypnotic trance.

Usually, a stage hypnotist will select a suggestible subject who will be willing to comply with his instructions for fear of letting the entertainer or the audience down. The person is being psychologically intimidated. The person may even be convinced that they have been hypnotised or he or she might have been hypnotised prior to the stage performance.

But to return to the point I am making that everyone retains his or her free will during and after actual hypnotism, there is an example that I can think of that might cause some people to doubt the veracity of my claims, that being a demonstration of hypnotism by celebrated illusionist Derren Brown.

The exercise was recorded for a television show and leaving aside any trickery that television recording might afford a performing artist, this was an impressive piece of showmanship.

The show was first broadcast in the UK on C4 as the first in a series entitled Derren Brown: The Experiments.

It involved a subject, who, I have no reason to doubt, had been hypnotised earlier. Having been hypnotised he then took a pistol and shot the broadcaster Stephen Fry on stage when prompted to do so and immediately forgot his actions.

He had been informed while in a trance that his gun was loaded with real bullets and not blanks (though this was not the case – the shells were, indeed, blanks).

Unless my insistence that a hypnotised subject cannot be compelled to act out of character is wrong, it would seem I was stating that Mr Brown's subject was willing to become a cold-blooded killer and gun down Mr Fry in front of a theatre audience.

Mr Brown's selection of subject is not necessarily insignificant but I will ignore this. What I am saying is that Mr Brown's fame and popularity was the deciding factor in why the experiment could work.

Although a normal member of the public seemed to have been instructed while in a hypnotic trance into becoming a celebrity's assassin, I would contend that because of the subject's faith and trust in Derren Brown he was able to carry out the assassination confident in his unconscious mind that no matter how bizarre Mr Brown's instructions might seem, Mr Brown was a man of enough integrity to ensure that no harm would come to anyone nor any law be broken.

To further understand the methodology of stage hypnotism, readers might care to refer to psychology theories such as those debated following the famous obedience experiments conducted by Yale University psychologist Stanley Milgram in 1961 and replicated since then elsewhere. Milgram sought to measure the willingness of participants to obey the orders of an authority figure.

Stage hypnosis is based on manipulation. And some politicians use similar techniques, an extreme example being Adolf Hitler. How often was he described as a mesmerising speaker? He manipulated a nation.

At the other end of the spectrum, there are sales people who often follow well-rehearsed routines to vend their products.

Clinical hypnosis, though, is about free will – allowing participants to rationalise and understand themselves. Conducted correctly it is a powerful tool for good.

Power of Now *(Page 41)*

The Power of Now is the title of a book by Ekhart Tolle that popularised a way of thinking rooted in ancient philosophies and religions and is widely recognised by hypnotherapists. It propounds that our past and our future are in our unconscious mind and all that exists is the here and now.

People might look to the future and think: "I'll be happy once I've paid off the mortgage or if I win the lottery."

They may even achieve their target yet continue to look ahead and so never reach self-actualisation.

Likewise, people look to the past and they identify with who they thought themselves to have been in their past – but their memory is distorted because the unconscious plays tricks on us.

We are what we are now. To look ahead with the power of now is not thinking: "I'll be happy WHEN" but being happy now.

The boxer who enjoys his training NOW might become a champion because of that training; the dieter who eats and thinks like a ten-stone person will one day become that person; the smoker who stops is a non-smoker NOW and so will be so in the future.

People in a hypnotic trance are in the NOW and they are happy.

You can plan ahead but bring it to the NOW.

Anxiety and excitement *(Pages 65, 78, 89 &*
91)

Picture two people queuing for a roller coaster
ride.

One says he is anxious, the other that he is
excited.

Both of them are in the same condition.

The one who says he is anxious might describe
the physical sensation that he is experiencing as
tingling in his fingers, heart racing. He is
reluctant for people to notice he is anxious. The
demands he places on himself exacerbate his
feelings. He is anxious about being anxious.

The person who says he is excited might
describe the physical sensation he is
experiencing as tingling in his fingers, heart
racing. He is happy to show his excitement. He
is embracing his emotion and physical feelings
of adrenalin instead of panicking.

FREQUENTLY ASKED QUESTIONS

How long will it be after my session with a hypnotherapist before I can call myself a non-smoker?

You will be a non-smoker with immediate effect. There is no "qualifying period".

What's the difference between stage hypnosis and hypnotherapy?

The distinction is explained in this book. Stage hypnosis is not regarded as hypnosis by clinical hypnotherapists and no therapist who is a member of the British Society of Clinical Hypnosis is permitted to participate in stage hypnosis.

What does the term hypnosis mean?

The word hypnosis derives from the Greek god Hypnos whose name meant sleep. In its modern sense, the term hypnosis was first used in 1843 by Scottish surgeon James Braid, regarded by many as the first genuine hypnotherapist. He employed the term to describe a sleep-like state which embraced both keen awareness and receptiveness. The name hypnosis is now a recognised title though some might say a better description would be meditative therapy.

Will I know if I am in a hypnotic trance?

When driving a car, a driver may turn up at their destination and think "how did I get here?"

They have been driving on "automatic pilot". The unconscious mind has taken over. This is not anything to be concerned about. We function perfectly well, if not better when we allow our unconscious minds to guide us. We have to trust our unconscious minds.

There are different reasons why people may decide to enter meditative trances.

Some people enter meditative trances just to relax.

Others use it for reflective therapeutic reasons, which is the essence of hypnotherapy.

Will a hypnotherapist have control over me when I'm in a trance?

Some individuals use the meditative trance state for religious or spiritual reasons. Many Christians will go into reflective alert trance states while praying. Other Christians who practise prayer frequently may enter a deeper meditative trance.

Buddhist Monks are good examples of how a meditative trance works.

When a Buddhist Monk initially begins to practise meditation they are usually guided by their mentors.

I am guiding patients into a meditative trance. Nobody can be forced into a meditative trance without that person's consent or willingness. Everyone can enter a trance if they wish to do so, however.

Imagine now that a Buddhist Monk is meditating in a room by himself. His conscious mind has drifted into tranquillity. His unconscious mind, however, is listening to everything around him.

If he was to hear people walking into the room, his unconscious mind would alert his conscious mind. He may be concerned and listen consciously to who it is entering the room. For argument's sake, picture that it is his friends' voices he hears.

He will recognise there is no danger so he re-enters a deeper state of trance. His friends may walk into the far corner of the room and continue their conversation. The Buddhist monk's conscious mind is not listening to what they are saying and he is in a tranquil state, however, his unconscious mind is listening to every word that is been said without him realising it. If his friend were to state suddenly that the building was on fire, the monk's unconscious would be concerned and immediately alert the conscious mind to awaken and exit the building.

When clients come to see me, they are in full control. Their unconscious will always look after them and, of course, I can only give them positive beneficial suggestions. Their unconscious minds will awaken them immediately if I was to say anything harmful. A patient can open their eyes at any point if they wish to do so.

Patients are aware of sounds inside and outside of the room. If an aeroplane is to fly by, the patient may become aware of this consciously and distinguish that it is not a danger so there is no need to be concerned. They will then re-enter the meditative trance state.

If the fire alarm was to suddenly go off, or if they needed the toilet desperately, the unconscious will be concerned and alert the conscious mind to awaken immediately.

I've smoked for years. How do I know hypnosis is going to work?

It will work if you want it to work. If you have decided it is time to quit then the resolve is integrated into your unconscious by the hypnotherapist.

I started smoking when I was in my teens and after nearly 50 years I'm wondering if it's just too late to give up?

It's never too late to adopt healthier habits, in fact, the more vulnerable we become because of age the more important it is to adopt healthy choices. Remember, there will be immediate benefits for your health when you stop and the longer-term risks associated with smoking will also decline over time.

Why does treatment cost so much?

An obvious point to make is that compared to the cost of smoking over even a short period of time, a hypnotherapist's fee is modest.

The therapist also has bills to pay and needs to charge a fee. In addition, though, the therapist's fee imposes a sacrifice on the client that helps focus his or her mind and urges him or her to grasp responsibility.

BIBLIOGRAPHY

ANONYMOUS 2013. Tobacco control: when economics trumps health. Lancet, 382, 182.

BANDURA, A Self-efficacy: toward a unifying theory of behavioral change. Psychological Review, 84, 191-215.

BARBER, J (1996). Hypnosis and suggestion in the treatment of pain; a clinical guide. N.Y. Norton Company Inc.

BARNETT, EA (1992). The ideomotor signal/ repeated induction technique (for the rapid induction of deep hypnosis) revised version (1991). Australian Journal of Clinical Hypnotherapy and Hypnosis,13(1), 9-14.

BUCKNER, JD & VINCI, C (2013). Smoking and social anxiety: the roles of gender and smoking motives. Addictive Behaviors, 38, 2388-91.

CABALLO, VE (Ed.) (1998). International handbook of cognitive and behavioural treatments for psychological disorder: Pregamon.

CARR, A The Easy Way to Stop Smoking.

CRAWFORD, HJ, BROWN, AM, & MOON, CE (1993). Sustained attention and disattentional abilities: Differences between low and highly hypnotisable persons. Journal of Abnormal Psychology, 102(4), 534-543.

DAVEY, GCL (Ed), (1997). Phobias, Handbook of Theory, Research and Treatment: Wiley.

DOWD, T (2000). Cognitive Hypnotherapy. Maryland, USA: Aronson.

DRYDEN, W (1991). Reason And Therapeutic Change. London: Whurr Publishers Ltd.

DRYDEN, W (1995a). Practical Skills in Rational Emotive Behaviour Therapy: Preparing For Client Change. London: Whurr Publishers Ltd.

DRYDEN, W (1995b). Practical Skills in Rational Emotive Behaviour Therapy: Facilitating Client Change in Rational Emotive Behaviour Therapy. London: Whurr Publishers Ltd.

DRYDEN, W (1995c). Brief Rational Emotive Behaviour Therapy. England: John Wiley & Sons Ltd

DRYDEN, W & ELLIS, A (1995). Dilemmas in giving warmth or love to clients. In S. Palmer, W. Dryden, A. Ellis, & R. Yapp (Eds.), Rational interviews. London: Centre for Rational Emotive Behaviour Therapy.

DRYDEN, W & NEENAN, M (1996). Dictionary of Rational Emotive Behaviour Therapy. London: Whurr Publishers Ltd.

ECKHART, T (1999).The Power of Now: A guide to spiritual enlightenment. Namaste Publishing and New World Library Novato, California.

ELLIS, A (1962). Reason and emotion in psychotherapy. New York: Lyle Stuart.

ELLIS, A (1986). Anxiety about anxiety: The use of hypnosis with rational-emotive therapy. In ET Dowd & JM Healy (Eds), Case studies in hypnotherapy (pp. 3 -11). New York: Guilford Press.

ELLIS, A (1988). How to stubbornly refuse to make yourself miserable about anything – yes anything! Secaucus, NJ: Lyle & Stuart.

ELLIS, A (1989). The treatment of psychotic and borderline individuals with RET. (Orig, publication, 1965) New York: Institute for Rational Emotive and Cogniotive Behaviour Therapy, 9 139-172.

ELLIS, A (1993). Rational-emotive imagery and hypnosis. In J. W. Rhue, S. J. Lynn, & I Kirsch (Eds.), Handbook of clinical hypnosis(pp. 173-86). Washington, DC: American Psychological Association.

ELLIS, A, GORDON, J, NEENAN M, & PALMER, S (1997). Stress counselling: A rational emotive behaviour approach. London: Cassell.

ELLIS, A & GRIEGER, R (Eds.). Handbook of rational-emotive therapy (2 vols.). New York: Springer.

ERICKSON, MH (1980 in EL Rossi (ed.). The collected papers of Milton H. Erickson on Hypnosis Volume II. Hypnotic alteration of sensory, perceptual and psychological processes. New York: Irvington.

ERICKSON, MH (1980 in EL Rossi (ed.). The collected papers of Milton H. Erickson on Hypnosis Volume I. The nature of hypnosis and suggestion. New York: Irvington.

ERICKSON, MH (1980 in EL Rossi (ed.). The collected papers of Milton H. Erickson on Hypnosis Volume IV. Innovative hypnotherapy. New York: Irvington.

ERICKSON, MH (1952/1980). Deep hypnosis and its induction. In E Rossi (Ed.), The Collected Papers of Milton H. Erickson on Hypnosis. I. The Nature of Hypnosis and Suggestions (pp. 139- 167). New York: Irvington.

FRANKLIN, RL (2004). The Mythology of Self Worth: howtobooks.

GILBERT, P (1997). Overcomoing Depression: Robinson.

GRINDLER, J & BANDLER, R (1981). Tranceformations. Utah: Real People Press

HAMMOND, DC (Ed.). (1990). Handbook of hypnotic suggestions and metaphors. New York: WW Norton & Company.

HALEY, J (1973). Uncommon Therapy: The psychiatric techniques of Milton H. Erickson, M.D. (Paperback edition). New York: Norton.

HARTLAND, J (1971). Medical and dental hypnosis and its clinical applications. London: Bailliere Tindall.

HAUK, PA (1971). An RET theory of depression. Rational Living, 6(2), 32 -35.

HAUCK, PA (1973). Overcoming depression. Philadelphia:Westminter.

HAUK. PA (1991). Hold your head up high. London: Sheldon.

HEAP, M (1988). Hypnosis: Current clinical, experimental, and forensic practices. New York: Routledge.

HILGARD, ER (1986). Divided consciousness: Multiple controls in human thought and action (expanded ed.). New York: Wiley.

HILGARD, ER & HILGARD, JR (1994). Hypnosis in the relief of pain (Rev. Ed.). N. Y. Brunner/ Mazel.

HOWE, D (1993). On Being a Client: Understanding the Process of Counselling and Psychotherapy. London: Sage.

HUNTER, R (1995).The Art of Hypnotherapy. Iowa: Kendall/ Hunt Publishing Company.

JOSEPH, A (2009). Cognitive Behavioural Therapy: Your route out of perfectionism, self-sabotage and other everyday habits. Capstone Publishing Ltd. (a Wiley Company) The Atrium, Southern Gate, Chirchester.

KIRSCH, I (1993). Cognitive behavioural hypnotherapy. In handbook of Clinical Hypnosis, ed. JW Rhue, SJ Lynn and Kirsch, pp. 151- 172. Washington, DC: American Psychological Association.

KIRSCH, I, MONTOGMERY, G, AND SAPIRSTEIN, G (1995). Hypnosis as an adjunct to cognitive behavioural psychotherapy: a meta- analysis. Journal of Consulting and Clinical Psychology 63:214-220.

KROGER, WS (1977). Clinical and experimental hypnosis. Philadelphia: J. B. Lippincott.

LEWIS. CS (1944) Mere Christianity. A revised and amplified edition, with a new introduction, of the three books, Broadcast Talks, Christian Behaviour and Beyond Personality. HarperCollins.

LIBERMAN, MA, YALOM, ED & MILES, MB (1973). Encounter Groups: First Facts. N. Y. Basic Groups.

MARTINAZ, E, TATUM, KL, GLASS, M, BERNATH, A, FERRIS, D, REYNOLDS, P & SCHNOLL, RA Correlates of smoking cessation self-efficacy in a community sample of smokers. Addictive Behaviors, 35, 175-8.

MCMASTER, NL (1992). One clinician's view of the hypnotherapeutic encounter. Australian Journal of Clinical Hypnotherapy and Hypnosis, 13(2), 77-85.

MCMASTER, NL (1996). Major depression: A hypno-cognitive- behavioural intervention. Australian Journal of Clinical Hypnotherapy and Hypnosis, 17 (1), 17-24.

MILGRAM, S (1963). Behavioral study of obedience. Journal of Abnormal and Social Psychology, 67, 371-8.

NEENAN, M & DRYDEN, W (1999). Rational Emotive Behaviour Therapy; Advances in Theory & Practice. London: Whurr Publishers Ltd.

REBER, SR (1985). The Penguin Dictionary of Psychology. Penguin Books.

SARGENT, JD, TICKLE, JJ, BEACH, ML, DALTON, MA, AHRENS, MB & HEATHERTON, TF BRAND appearances in contemporary cinema films and contribution to global marketing of cigarettes. Lancet, 357, 29-32.

WOLINSKY, S (1993). The Dark Side of the Inner Child. The Bramble Company.

WOLINSKY, S (1991) Trances People Live. The Bramble Company.

YANKURA, J(Ed) & DRYDEN, W (Ed.) (1997). Using REBT with common psychological problems: Springer.

YAPKO, MD (1989). Trancework: An introduction to the practice of clinical hypnosis. N. Y. Brunner/ Mazel.

ZILBERGELD, B, EDELSTEIN, MG, ARAOZ, DL (1986). Hypnosis: Questions & Answers. New York: Norton.